The Golden Mask of Agamemnon

A play for young people

John Wiles

Samuel French – London

New York – Sydney – Toronto – Hollywood

THE FIRST PRODUCTION

The Golden Masque of Agamemnon was commissioned by the Cockpit Arts Workshop (Inner London Education Authority) and first presented there as its eighth annual summer youth production in 1977, by the following company:

Catharine Alonso, Louise Allwood, Lila Anam, Alan Barrett, Hedda Beeby, Anna Bird, Irena Borzym, Elise Bugansky, Amanda Carmichael, Michael Collins, Carol Cooper, Anne Crowley, Gary Daly, Nigel Davies, Graham Dearing, John Denis, Catharine Doran, Julie Draper, Sally Dyson, Helen Edwards, Anjela Evans, Carlton Facey, Vanessa Fantie, Lewis Foti, Carla Grey, Augustus Hamilton, Gloria Hamilton, Charlotte Herxheimer, Rupert Hinton, Carol Johnson, Sukey Johnson, Rosemary Katzen, Miriam King, Florence Lang, Susan Lawes, Dawn Lewis, Sarah Linnett, Paul Loughran, Solly Mansoor, Bruce McCormack, Susan Moses, Kate O'Connell, Tina Olaloko, Helen Parkhurst, Anne Rodney, Michelle Rudolf, Sylvia Schloss, Nicky Scott, Adrian Silvertown, Penny Skeats, Matthew Stringer, Mary Suffren, Karen Swirsky, Colin Turner, Jessica van Niekerk, Catharine Woodger and Ian Yeoman.

Music by Peter West. *Set by* Roger Glossop & Dave Lovett. *Costumes by* Jean Clarke and Jessica Chappell. *Lighting by* John Coffey. *Movement by* Melanie Thompson. *Musical Direction by* Peter Collis. *Directed by* John Wiles.

INTRODUCTION

The Golden Masque is an attempt to bring together all the stories of Agamemnon in a way which will make them challenging, theatrical and evocative to young people who may never have heard of the Greek legends. The value of myth is discussed later in Rehearsal and Production Notes; it is enough to say that my chief aim was to provide as thrilling (and chilling) a production as possible.

It is written for a cast of any size. In its present version it calls for about forty speaking or singing parts, but many of those could be doubled. To keep this as fluid as possible, I've always encouraged as many people as possible to stay on the stage where they can and follow the unfolding of the legends with the same attention as the audience. When they are needed to slip off-stage and prepare for their next appearance, I've left to the discretion of the director and the circumstance at the time. Thus for a company that has an endless list of acting members, they can make definite entrances and exits. For those who only have a limited number of players available, they can do it as a "studio" performance, moving forward in view of the audience to "set-up" a new character. For example on page eight "menacing figures" could be anyone the director has available at the time; the same with "main cast" on page one, i.e. anybody who does not have to make a specific entrance a page or so later on or who is already dressed and made-up as a Trojan, and would therefore look wrong in the Greek setting.

The action is described for an in-the-round production, doing away with the need for more elaborate and expensive sets. Nevertheless, if facilities permitted, a much more spectacular staging could be envisaged. The main features described in the present script—a central scaffolding tower to give height, smoke, dry ice and so on—can all be adapted or abandoned.

The play is in two parts. In production the First Act ran sixty-eight minutes, the Second forty-nine.

The action starts in the Apollo sanctuary at Delphi and keeps returning there. The period is 1200 BC.

J.W.

THE GOLDEN MASQUE OF AGAMEMNON

List of Characters

Agamemnon, the King
Thybius, the Narrator
Calchas, the High Priest
The Pythoness
Clytemnestra, the Queen
Iphigenia
Macaria
Althaea
Alcmene
Melita
Hiera
Leucippe
Polydora
Hermione
Girl Dancer
Menelaus, Agamemnon's brother
Arab Dancer
Cilissa, the Nurse
Orestes
Electra

Chrysothemis
Aegisthus
Hermes
Warriors
Boys
Odysseus
King Nestor
Achilles
Hecuba, the Trojan Queen
Cassandra, her daughter
Three Girls
Watchman
Pylades
Remorse
Guilt
Shame
Regret
Palace Guards
Athene
Apollo
Singers

Soldiers, Townspeople, Attendants, Beggars, Court Ushers, Musicians, etc.

ACT I

The house lights go down

The Blood Curse

A sudden crack of thunder that is not quite thunder, which echoes and re-echoes through the hall. Before the sound has died—

Mist creeps across the floor. A smell of incense from the tripod. The music starts, an eerie sound that might be wailing accompanied by a single drumbeat that resembles the dripping of water or perhaps it is the dripping of water

The main cast enters in two lines and takes its place around the perimeter, kneeling on the floor. The actors lift their arms and link them. They start a rhythmical swaying which grows more abandoned as they struggle to speak. The sound we hear is not a pleasant one; it is as if they are trying to force it out between locked jaws

Girls Mm-mm-mm-mm . . .
Boys Ga-ga-ga-ga-ga . . .

The music builds like a wind rising. The struggle to say the word drives the actors to their feet. Now they stamp and begin to move more wildly. Their agony is doubled. The Lights and mist go red. Now it looks like blood spilling across the floor. The music rises to a climax. The actors triumphantly explode with the following cry, as the music breaks with a loud chord

All Aga-mem-*non*!

Silence

Agamemnon rises slowly through the mist. He is in full armour. In spite of the gleaming metal which seems to encase him completely, there is something unearthly about him, making him as unreal as the ghost of Hamlet's father. Even his voice, as it issues from the box-like helmet, sounds like a challenge from beyond the grave

Agamemnon Zeus! you that rule from Mount Ida, most glorious, most great. You, the sun! whose eye, whose ear miss nothing in this world. You Rivers and you Earth, you Powers of the world below that make the souls of dead men pay for perjury—all these mark the question I put to the god.
All (*echoing like wild birds crying*) Mark . . . mark . . . mark.

Thybius clambers down the scaffolding into view

Thybius (*to the audience*) His name is Agamemnon. He is commander of all the Greeks.

Agamemnon Twelve long months our fleet has waited to sail against Troy. Twelve long months our men have stayed on the beach eating their hearts out in boredom. Twelve long months our ships and ropes have rotted in the water while cowards creep away, but still, still the wind blows against us.

Thybius (*as before*) It's true. For nearly a year we've tried to launch this attack against Troy. Why, from this crow's nest of mine, I can see all the ships—nigh on a thousand of them—reeling over from the gale that won't even let them out of the harbour. So long they've been like that it looks as if they're growing there.

Agamemnon (*falling to his knees*) What have we done?

Calchas (*a magnified call from outside*) Agamemnon?

Thybius (*excited*) That's Calchas, the High Priest.

Calchas (*as before*) Put your question to the god.

Agamemnon Then, how have we offended him, and what must we do to gain the South wind for Troy?

Calchas First one and then the other, you shall be told.

The mist is clearing. The Lights change as dawn approaches. The Attendants lead Calchas into the temple

Attendants   Zeus, where e'er you be,
This you shall be called of me,
If this name you love to bear
Great king of earth and sea and air.

One there was who reigned of old,
Now his name is no more told,
Huge with wrath and filled with hate,
Great Zeus at last rules in his place.

Calchas Bring me the portent.

Agamemnon kneels in front of the Priest and removes his helmet. As the first offering is made, Thybius speaks. He is bursting with impatience to tell the audience

Thybius It seems to me you don't know enough. First, we're in Greece, right on the very edge of it. Over there—beyond those walls—at a place called Aulis, the thousand ships have been gathered to take Agamemnon's troops to Troy. Why Troy, you ask? I'll tell you. Menelaus, Agamemnon's younger brother—that's him there standing by the commander—has had his wife Helen stolen from him by a Trojan prince, Paris by name. Of course he wants to get her back, so he and his brother have collected all the armed men of Greece to attack Troy. (*Furiously*) The trouble is the gods won't send us the right wind to get us there.

Calchas (*a sung line*) Blood, nothing but blood! (*Spoken*) Bring me another. There is no liver in this bird.

Agamemnon No liver? What does that mean?

Calchas That you have offended Artemis. It is she who sends the North wind against you.

During this time an Attendant has held a bowl of drugged smoke close to the Priest. While another bird is prepared, he inhales deeply

Agamemnon But what have I done to offend her?

Calchas Once on a stag-hunt, you killed a beast with one blow of your long-shadowed spear, did you not?

Agamemnon (*boasting*) That's happened many times.

Calchas But did you not say, "Artemis herself could not have done better"?

Agamemnon A joke! She cannot be angry with me for that!

Calchas (*swaying now*) Give me the other bird. (*He digs the knife into the second offering and tears it open. Another sung line*) Again no liver!

All Blood . . . blood!

The music quickens. A general movement of restlessness

Agamemnon (*shocked*) What does *that* mean?

Calchas Worse than I thought. The goddess invokes the blood curse of Atreus.

The Girls scream and hide their faces. The Boys chant five times

Boys Blood . . . blood . . . blood . . . blood . . . blood!

The earth groans. Thunder. The Lights turn green

Thybius (*shouting to the audience over the growing uproar*) Listen now, this is important!

Calchas starts stamping and swaying. The drug is taking effect. His dance is not one of flowing lines, but of jerking movements, contorted, reflecting the images he sees

Calchas Two men . . .

All (*a shout*) Two men!

Calchas One Atreus——

Agamemnon My father?

Calchas —the other, his brother Thyestes.

Agamemnon My uncle!

Some of the cast run forward with masks. As Calchas recites his narrative, the story is acted in mime. More time is taken than is shown here. The lines are torn from Calchas at long intervals

Calchas (*wracked with visions, writhing on the floor or stretching high*) Two brothers, both sons of Pelops, grandsons of Tantalus intimate of the old gods who ruled before Zeus . . . but with only hatred between them . . . Atreus, father of Agamemnon, seized Argos and then took Aerope to wife . . . Thyestes lusted for her and won her . . . Atreus discovered this, went wild with rage . . . Thyestes was driven from Argos, leaving his sons behind . . . days passed, months . . . Atreus invited Thyestes to return, saying, "All has been forgiven" . . . a meal was prepared, a huge pie . . .

containing the hacked-up bodies of Thyestes' sons! (*A howl of horror*) Oh, curse of brothers! When Atreus told him what he'd eaten, Thyestes laid the curse against him. Nothing but blood would come of his line ...

All (*following intently; a whisper*) The blood curse of the House of Atreus ...

Calchas (*quieter now*) One son remained, the child Aegisthus, seven years old ... Atreus said, pretending to be his father, "You must kill uncle Thyestes" ... Thyestes woke to find his own son standing over him with a sword! "What is this? I am your father!"

All (*as before*) Your father ...!

Calchas (*fevered now, agitated*) "He is the one you must kill, Atreus. Take that sword and for the sake of your little slaughtered brothers, sink it in your uncle's guts!" Aegisthus, seven years old, did so. He killed Agamemnon's father!

Agamemnon (*a loud cry*) May the gods curse him!

Calchas Agamemnon drove Aegisthus and his father from Argos once again.

Agamemnon Justice, justice, nothing but justice!

Calchas Was it justice what your father did? Giving Thyestes of his own sons to eat?

Agamemnon He'd slept with my father's wife! Anyway, he had his revenge. He had my father killed. The blood curse is at an end.

Calchas Aegisthus still lives, a grown man now.

Agamemnon But far away. I seek no vengeance on him for killing my father. I ask only a wind to Troy to get my soldiers there.

Calchas Is Menelaus not your brother, another son of Atreus?

Agamemnon He is.

Calchas Then the curse still holds good, and the North wind blows and blows.

Agamemnon (*tormented*) What can we do to lay it in the dust? We have no quarrel with Aegisthus now. It's this new insult from the Trojans which concerns us more.

The Lights have been slowly returning to normal. Calchas is also recovering

Calchas (*almost sadly*) I can't tell you. It's too big a thing for a mere priest ...

Thybius (*to the audience*) Mark this priest. Some don't trust him. He was once a Trojan himself. By consulting the Oracle here at Delphi he learnt how Greece would one day conquer Troy, so in fear—some say—he stayed on here, and now he's more Greek than the Greeks.

Agamemnon (*to Calchas*) Then there is a way?

Calchas Do not ask me.

Agamemnon Then summon the Oracle herself! All Greece pants to wage this war against Troy. We must have a wind to take our ships there. Whatever Artemis and the other gods demand in payment, *we must be told.*

Calchas (*to the Attendants*) Call her ...

The Pythoness (*an electronic voice that echoes from all sides of the theatre*) I am here.

All The Pythoness ... the Pythoness ... (*They prostrate themselves in fear*)

She enters, a figure entirely swathed in white veils. No face can be seen but her voice continues to be magnified so that it still seems to be coming from all sides of the theatre. As she speaks, her Attendants perform a frieze of movement

The Pythoness Agamemnon?

Agamemnon Mother of us all, voice of the god himself.

The Pythoness You have four children?

Agamemnon Four apples of my eye. Orestes, my son, and three daughters each fairer than the other.

Thybius (*to the audience*) Remember these names.

Agamemnon Electra, Iphigenia and Chrysothemis, innocents all, beloved of their mother.

The Pythoness   If Troy must fall
                                 And fall she must,
                                 One of these
                                 Must come to dust.

Agamemnon O, god, no!

A wailing from the Girls

Boys (*beating in time on the floor*) Blood ... blood ... blood ... blood ... blood.

The Pythoness Iphigenia must die, here at the alter. The goddess demands it.

Boys Blood ... blood ... blood ... blood ... blood ... (*Break off*)

The Pythoness Refuse and the wind continues. Agree—sacrifice your child—and it will change. However, you have one alternative.

Agamemnon (*a cry*) Tell me!

The Pythoness Hand over the command of the army to another, return home, plough your fields. Let Troy fall without you.

Agamemnon Let others lead the victory against Troy, you mean?

The Pythoness You have the choice.

Agamemnon Never!

The Pythoness As always the gods leave the decision to man. But the result of his decision rests upon his own head, squarely there.

Agamemnon I have made my choice. It is *my* army.

The Pythoness Be warned, blood follows blood. The curse which started with your father and even further back in time, is not over yet. Kill your daughter as commanded, but as ripple surely follows ripple when a stone is cast, more blood and yet more blood must flow.

Agamemnon Is it shown in the Oracle that I shall lead the victory against Troy?

The Pythoness After nine more years, yes.

Agamemnon Then there is your answer. (*To his Officers*) Send for my daughter Iphigenia. She will be killed as the goddess demands. After that, one good turn deserving another, the wind will change and we'll sail for Troy.

All (*a battle-cry*) For Troy!

A crash of sound. All Lights go down except for the spotlight on Thybius

Thybius I know these things because I was there. Thybius is my name, Talthybius in full. You'll find it in the history books. I was Agamemnon's page. Did these things really happen, you ask. Did I really exist? Ah ... what is history but myth, and what is myth but a story passed from lip to lip? But be assured of this—if belief can make a thing happen, *this happened.* You can see Troy still ... well, the dust of it anyway. You can certainly see the Lion Gate at Mycenae. It was in the palace there that Queen Clytemnestra heard that her husband was sending for their daughter Iphigenia.

Clytemnestra (*suspiciously*) What does he want with her?

Thybius (*kneeling*) A betrothal, great Queen. She is to be wedded to the beloved of the gods, heroic Achilles himself.

Clytemnestra (*impressed*) Achilles?

Thybius (*to the audience*) Actually Agamemnon tried to warn his wife, telling her on no account to let me have the girl, but his brother Menelaus, anxious for the sacrifice, intercepted the letter and ordered me—on pain of death—to hold my tongue. Knowing Menelaus, I held it.

Clytemnestra What does great Achilles say?

Thybius Lady, he wishes nothing better. (*To audience*) Actually he knew nothing about it.

Clytemnestra Very well, she will be brought to you. May Zeus bless this happy union.

Thybius (*piously*) Amen to that. (*Rising briskly*) So Iphigenia was delivered to me and I conveyed her with due alacrity to Aulis where that damned North wind was still blowing.

SCENE 2

The Sacrifice

The wind blows. Sunlight falls on the hard earth. The Chorus prepares for the sacrifice, speaking as they mime

Macaria This is the place where the girl must die.

All Scrub the wood, scour the stone.

Althaea Purify the altar with holy wreaths of flowers.

Alcmene Sprinkle the floor with water.

Boys Away with lamentation!

Boy 1 She dies in a good cause, doesn't she?

Boy 2 The sooner she dies the better.

Melita Poor child.

Boy 3 For the quicker she dies, the quicker we'll hoist sail for Troy.

Boys To the war!

Chorus (*singing*)   Apollo, Healer, Saviour,
                              Apollo, son of Zeus,
                              Blest be thy name, Apollo!

Hiera Sorrow, sing sorrow, but let good prevail.

Boy 4 Man must suffer to be wise.

Boy 5 Oh, I don't know. These are fairly enlightened days on the whole. Now in the old times——

Leucippe —in the days of Ouranos and Gaia, Cronos and Prometheus——

Boy 6 —and before them, the even older gods Tammuz and Ishtar, Attis and Cybele——

Polydora Man was never allowed a choice. Everything was chaos and disorder and the gods ruled without reason.

Boy 7 It was do this, do that, all the time, and woe betide you if you didn't jolly well get on and do it.

Hermione Vengeance, vengeance was all.

Boy 5 Now at least things are better. With Zeus and the others you're allowed a choice. Of course you still have to do what they want——

Boy 7 —or you'll catch it just the same. So the ends haven't changed. It's just the means which are different.

Chorus (*singing*)   Apollo, Healer, Saviour,
                                    Apollo, son of Zeus,
                                    Blest be thy name, Apollo!

Boy 1 (*to audience*) I ask you, what choice does Agamemnon have?

Macaria He could give up command of the army to someone else, couldn't he?

The Boys laugh scornfully

Boy 2 And be branded a coward for life? Never!

A Girl (*defiantly*) I'll dance for the girl.

Boy 3 Women's games!

Several of the Chorus beat out a rhythm with pebbles held in their hands. The Girl dances in mourning, a simple series of movements, dipping, flowing, arms held extended or stiffly at the sides as in the decoration on Greek vases. Others join in. Everything should be kept as simple as possible. After a while another Girl sings against the beat, a jaunty little number

Girl   Weep for a mother
                             Deceived by a king.
                             Weep, mother,
                             Die king.

                             Bloodshed bringing in its train
                             Kindred blood that flows again.
                             Die, mother,
                             Die king.

                             Weep for a king
                             Who's killed by his wife.
                             Weep, king,
                             Die, wife.

                             Weep for a mother
                             Slain by her son.
                             Die, mother,
                             Die, wife.

Heavier music starts as if to emphasize the prophecy in the little song. The dance breaks up as the Procession approaches. Calchas enters first, leading Iphigenia by the hand. Perhaps other young girls attend her. Then come Agamemnon, Menelaus, Thybius and other menacing figures of importance

As if to reassert itself the wind howls more loudly

Agamemnon (*nervously to Menelaus*) What if the wind still does not change?
Menelaus Believe, brother. How can the gods do their share if we don't
    believe in them?

The Procession moves round the arena and approaches the altar. One of the Girls sets up a wailing to the music which gives it an Arabic or North African flavour

Girl   Cry, sorrow, sorrow . . .
                      But let good prevail.

The drums take up the hint of Africa and a new rhythm emerges, faster now, raising the temperature of the blood

                      Sorrow, sing sorrow . . .
                      But good prevail, prevail.

Girls   Sorrow, sing sorrow . . .
                      But good prevail, prevail.
Iphigenia O, gods, grant me release from this long anxiety. Father, I beseech
    you—
Agamemnon (*unable to face her*) Bring a gag, some of you, and press her
    sweet mouth tightly with a chord.
Iphigenia Why do you turn away? Is it true what my senses tell me? Do you
    mean to kill me? Yet they told me it was to be my marriage day.
Menelaus My sweet niece and child—
Agamemnon O, ye gods, take her swiftly, swiftly—

The Girls start up an African wail again

Girl   Cry, sorrow, sorrow . . .
                      But let good prevail.

Girls   Cry, sorrow, sorrow . . .
                      But let good prevail.

Girl   Sorrow, sing sorrow . . .
                      But good prevail, prevail.

Girls   Sorrow, sing sorrow . . .
                      But good prevail, prevail.

A half-naked Boy hung about with beads and charms of all kinds carries a knife to Calchas. A conical straw hat hangs at his back. He is definitely more Arab than Greek. He kisses the knife and hands it to the Priest who lifts it high for blessing. Iphigenia gives a cry of alarm and turns to run. Instantly other figures set on her and she is bound to a frame and gagged. The Girls set up an ululation. The Boys beat the floor with their hands in time to the throbbing drums. The Arab Boy begins to dance, savagely and obscenely. The ululation continues

Calchas (*against all this, half-sung, half-said*) Zeus, whose will commands the only place where wisdom dwells, stay with your hand, marked by this blood, those ill-winds that check our ship of state and bring all reeling with thwarted vengeance. Artemis, great daughter of a greater god, moderate your fury for this poor King here and lean kindly to our side.

Iphigenia is lifted on the frame over the heads of the Attendants

Agamemnon (*a cry of agony*) For the god's sake, kill her!

Calchas strikes with the knife. Instantly the singing and the music stop

Black-out

In the darkness, the only sound which carries over is that of the remorseless North wind

After three seconds the lights return. Blood pours from (a bladder concealed at) Iphigenia's side. The Attendants fill three bowls with the blood. The Arab Boy dips his fingers in one and decorates his face and body with the stuff. Everybody watches hypnotized except for Agamemnon who has buried his face in his brother's shoulder. Some Girls sob. The Boys stare enthralled. The Arab Boy runs round proudly showing off the blood smears and daring others to touch them. The dead Iphigenia is lowered to the floor. Calchas dedicates the three bowls of blood

Calchas Now, great Artemis, accept our three libations. The first to the Olympian gods ... the second to the ancient heroes ... the third to the father of all things living and dead, Zeus, the ruler of the universe. (*He pours the blood on to the earth*)

A long silence

Agamemnon What if the wind does not die?

A long pause. The wind slowly dies

Thybius It has died! It has died! Zeus be praised. (*He scrambles up the scaffolding*)

Excitement. Cries of praise from all. Thybius shouts from the tower. They quieten to listen

Thybius I can see the ships bobbing at their anchors, no longer reeling over wind-struck, but upright now. All is still ... the men on the beach look up amazed, their left sides no longer wind-blasted.

A new wind starts

And now the waves begin their dance the other way. The ships heel over. The men feel the breeze on their right-hand flanks. The South wind! The South wind has started to blow us to Troy.

Agamemnon O, thank the god, thank the god.

Rejoicing from everybody

All To Troy! To Troy!

Calchas (*to Attendants*) Bear her away. She has done her share for the Greeks.

(*They take her out*)

Great King! Remember what the Pythoness said. Blood follows blood. All is not over yet. It's just begun.

Agamemnon War *is* the time for blood, priest. To the ships, proud soldiers of Greece. We sail for Troy this night!

Thybius (*less excited now*) Yes, we sailed for Troy that night. Some of us had heard from the Oracle that we'd be away nine years—Odysseus for twenty!—but none of us cared that night. After all that hanging about on the beach, what a joy to be on our way at last. (*Looking round*) But not everybody rejoiced. Clytemnestra, for example, didn't rejoice that night.

Clytemnestra Dead? Now by the great gods I swear a vengeance that will be handed on till the end of time. My beloved daughter dead?

Macaria Weep for a mother deceived by a king.

Clytemnestra Slew his daughter that he might go to Troy? Ye gods, I think I am going mad with fury. Listen, Zeus, if you did ever love *my* mother— that Leda you ravished in the shape of a swan—hear this mother's curse.

Althaea Weep for a mother deceived by a king.

Chorus Weep, mother, die, king.

Clytemnestra Death! That is my curse. Death by this hand. Or if not by this hand then let him know that even now his very juice of life is drying up.

A single spotlight shows Agamemnon waking up from a nightmare. He feels his heart, covers his face, weeps silently

In this very instant he is dying. No matter where he is nor in what strong health he stands, now the cells of his body are beginning their stealthy revolt. His eyes glaze, his veins close up, his lungs begin to gather phlegm, the muscles of his heart stagger once—they will never be so strong again.

Thybius comes to Agamemnon and calms him. The spotlight slowly fades

All Greece is dying, Agamemnon, for as its king and leading prince you have reached the peak and now descend the other side. And Clytemnestra rejoices. Better by far to find your death beneath the wall of Troy than face her fury. Death to the father, death to the king. Death to the husband who has slain a mother's love. Death.

Boy 1 The Pythoness said it. The Pythoness meant it.

Boy 2 Blood brings blood.

Alcmene Agamemnon was given the choice and chose to ignore it.

Melita The blood curse of Atreus goes on and on. Thyestes spoke it. Is there no end?

Boy 3 Wait, wait till Aegisthus appears.

Hiera Will it end then?

Boy 4 No, not for another twenty years.

Clytemnestra (*calling*) Nurse! Cilissa! Fetch my children and bring me mourning veils.

Several of the Chorus run forward and wrap her in white veils so that only her face is seen. Cilissa comes in as if shepherding three little children before her. She is already elderly

Cilissa Come, my little ones, come to your mother.

The adult Orestes, Electra and Chrysothemis appear on the edge of the action and watch. Clytemnestra falls on her knees and mimes caresses for the children

Clytemnestra Oh, my dear ones, my poor remaining children. Will he butcher you also?

Leucippe (*explaining*) The three remaining children of Clytemnestra— Orestes, Electra and Chrysothemis. Not as grown as you see them there; infants still, their reason shaken by their mother's grief.

Clytemnestra Would he take you too?

Cilissa Don't, mistress, you are frightening them.

Clytemnestra My poor Orestes, my dear son. How pale you are. Let me hold you. That scar on your brow, you have it still. You fell once while chasing a fawn with your sister. Let me brush it with my lips.

The adult Orestes touches the scar on his brow. Electra takes his hand and smiles

Cilissa Mistress, let me take them. They don't understand you.

Clytemnestra But this they understand. From this moment forth they have no father.

The adult Orestes falls to his knees

Orestes Alas, mother, has he been killed?

Clytemnestra (*to the mimed child*) In all but deed. (*To Cilissa*) Take them back into the palace. Now I have a whole new life to put on.

Cilissa Come, my little ones, my doves, my little fishes, this is no place for you.

She shepherds the infants out. Chrysothemis follows. Orestes lingers. Electra waits for him

Orestes (*as if in a dream*) But I think I shall remember it.

He and Electra go out

Polydora Does he? Does he remember it?

Boy 5 For twenty years he thinks of nothing else.

A voice speaks quietly, evilly from the shadows

Aegisthus Clytemnestra, do you remember me?

Boy 3 He is here. He has come.

Clytemnestra Who, who is it?

He steps forward, a menacing and sinister shape

Aegisthus (*a smile*) No, I do not think you remember me.
Hiera (*to Boy 3*) Is it him?
Boy 3 (*nodding*) Watch.
Clytemnestra Aegisthus ... son of Thyestes?
Aegisthus The very one.

The Chorus exhale as if they've been holding their breath

Aegisthus Hearing of your daughter's death ... and of your husband's departure for Troy ... I hastened to your side to bring you ... consolation.

Clytemnestra allows him to move up behind her. She leans back against him as he caresses her. The Chorus reacts

Hermione Oh, watch, she is nothing but a lecher.
Boy 6 Why not? She has no husband now.
Clytemnestra Did you not kill Agamemnon's father when you were only seven years old?
Aegisthus Where I killed once, I can again.

She turns and kisses him

Macaria See, see where she kisses him.
Clytemnestra I shall prepare his bed for you.

She goes out

Hermes (*speaking from the tower; quite quietly*) Aegisthus?
Althaea The god Hermes!

The Chorus reacts

Aegisthus (*unperturbed*) I know you, Hermes.
Hermes I bring you this warning from Zeus. Stop now, Aegisthus, before it is too late. Remember Orestes. Kill the father and the son. There will always be another son to carry the blood feud further.
Aegisthus (*in a sudden fury*) Atreus made my father *eat* his sons!
Hermes In dying by your hand Atreus paid the price.
Aegisthus Not enough. Does Zeus forbid my action?
Hermes Not forbid. You have the choice. But choose wrongly and the sin is yours.
Aegisthus Then my choice is made.
Hermes Justice should be tempered with pity and humanity. Moral good is the goal of all man's searching. Until that is obtained, the blood feud will go on and on.
Aegisthus That suits me. My mind's made up.

He goes out. Hermes shakes his head sadly and turns to the audience

Hermes You humans! Even the gods must bow to necessity sometimes, but here's this man ... (*He checks himself*) Well, remember this. Humility is needed when dealing with the gods. Mark that or you'll go like this man to your grave.

He goes

Fanfare. The Lights come up hard and bright. Thybius enters carrying basin and towels for Agamemnon's tent

SCENE 3

The Trojan Horse

Thybius (*to audience*) Welcome to sunny Troy.

Drums. Four Warriors leap into the arena—two Greek, two Trojan. A virile, dynamic dance involving two patrols, who creep and slide across the stage and then explode into an encounter in which the first pair soon die and the others hunt each other down like scared animals and finally kill each other. Thybius watches sadly from the sidelines, until eventually he speaks

It's been like that for nine years now. Beyond that rock—if you had but eyes to see it—is the city wall. Between it and the Greek camp which lies scattered all around, is a huge empty dusty plain. Every day sees scenes like this. (*To the corpses*) All right, get moving. Tomorrow you'll have to die like your brothers, the next day like your sons.

The Corpses leap to their feet and go. Thybius continues talking as he arranges cushions, wine flasks and towels in a tent area

So many people have died. I remember when we first heard from the Oracle how long it would take us to capture Troy, the king of Delos said—now there was a wily old bird for you—"Why don't you spend the first eight years here with me, and then just pop across to Troy in time for the victory?" I wish we had. It was a good idea.

Althaea Tell us about the war.

Thybius Boring, boring, boring.

Alcmene But there must be some fighting!

Thybius Oh, yes, Agamemnon fights Achilles and Achilles fights Agamemnon. Then Nestor fights Menelaus and everybody fights Odysseus. He's a bit thick, you see.

Melita But they're all on the same side!

Thybius That's right. In between we fight the Trojans. They do say Achilles has never forgiven the King for killing Iphigenia. He really thought he was going to marry her, you know, the day they finally produced her at Aulis. Here they come now. You'll see what I mean.

Agamemnon enters, followed by some of the generals. They have come straight from the battlefield. Thybius helps Agamemnon to clean up while the others throw themselves on the cushions and drink wine

Agamemnon (*pompously*) I positively refuse to take the field with Achilles again. He does nothing but laugh at my tactics.

Menelaus Truth to tell, brother, they are a bit laughable at times. That attack on the main gate. (*Wagging his head*) Oh, dear, oh, dear.

Agamemnon (*furiously*) It should have worked. If you hadn't rushed forward so early and pinned my men against the city wall——
Menelaus You were too slow, that's why.
Agamemnon Slow? I'll have you know——
Odysseus My trouble is I can never remember what I'm supposed to do.
Nestor Oh, Odysseus, how can you be so stupid? Sometimes I'm sure you don't know which side you're fighting on.
Agamemnon You can say that again, Nestor. He killed three of my best men last week.
Odysseus I know. I'm sorry, Agamemnon, I really am.
Menelaus Here comes Achilles now. You can blame him for everything.
Agamemnon I positively refuse to address a single word to him.

Achilles enters, a very sexy young man wearing only a gold jockstrap

I wish he'd put some clothes on. Very demoralizing for everybody when he appears in public like that.
Nestor You know these Myrmidons. Show-offs to a man.
Agamemnon It gives the Greeks such a bad name.
Achilles Ho, great king.
Agamemnon Ho yourself. If it's an apology you want, you've come to the wrong address. If you hadn't stood out there flashing your great shield in our eyes, we'd have all been in Priam's palace by dinnertime today.
Achilles I've found a way to end the war.
Nestor You what?
Odysseus What war?
All Oh, Odysseus!
Agamemnon Well, you needn't expect me to thank you. The whole thing would have ended years ago if you'd shown some co-operation.
Achilles (*furious*) Co-operation?
Agamemnon Put some clothes on for a start. Cover up your ... you know ...
Menelaus I suppose you'd better tell us, but I warn you I can't stay long. I'm meeting Paris in single combat at six o'clock.
Agamemnon Paris'll win. By seven they'll be dragging your body round the walls by the heels.
Menelaus Thanks very much!
Agamemnon And talking of heels, Achilles ... well, you'd better come in, I dare say, but wipe your feet first!

Achilles joins them and they talk silently

Melita Tell us about Agamemnon. Has he heard that Aegisthus has moved into his palace at Argos?
Thybius He's heard rumours, but he doesn't know what he's plotting.
Hiera And does he never think of his dead daughter, the one he killed so he could come to Troy?
Thybius Even Agamemnon isn't made of stone. You've seen one of his nightmares. He has them every night.
Leucippe They say his biggest fear is that the Oracle was wrong. That he'll never capture Troy and that Iphigenia was killed for nothing.

Thybius (*nodding*) They tell us justice can come from suffering. We must hope they're right. There's little hope for most of us if they're not.

He returns to the tent

Odysseus But what *is* a secret weapon?
All Oh, Odysseus!
Agamemnon Personally I don't trust Epeius. He's a Phocian from Parnassus, and anyone with all those p's in his name must be a phony.
Achilles He claims he had the message from Athene herself.
Agamemnon There you are. No goddess would talk to a Phocian. The man's a liar.
Menelaus But what form would this secret weapon take?
Achilles I'll show you.

He claps his hands and the Arab Boy from the earlier scene comes in carrying an object wrapped in a blanket

Menelaus (*to Agamemnon*) Here's another of them.
Agamemnon Damned nudists.

The Boy unwraps the object and reveals it to be a model of the Wooden Horse. A long pause. They examine it mystified

Nestor What is it?
Menelaus Does it go bang?
Achilles It's a horse.
Odysseus (*pleased*) Can I ride it?
Achilles A wooden horse.
Menelaus I'm sure it goes bang.
Agamemnon Whoever heard of a wooden horse?
Achilles The idea is to fill it with soldiers.
Menelaus They'd have to be very *little* soldiers.
Achilles (*growing angry*) It's a *model* wooden horse.
Agamemnon A model wooden . . .? Of course, anyone could see that.
Achilles We build a big one, you see, huge, bigger even than this tent and leave it on the beach and then we sail away. The Trojans think it's a gift from the gods, drag it into their city, and there we are.
Nestor Why should they do that? It seems a very silly thing to do.
Agamemnon Damned Phocians.
Menelaus I've had an idea for a secret weapon also. You hang something in the sky——
Achilles (*patiently*) Then when night comes, the soldiers come out of the horse, open the city gates, we return in the dark and the city is ours!
Agamemnon Yes, well . . . personally I don't trust any idea that can't be summarized on the back of a postage stamp.
Achilles (*losing his temper*) That's because that's the size of your head!
Menelaus Heigh-ho, I must be off to my fight with Paris.
Nestor I'll come along with you. You may need somebody to pick up the bits and pieces.

They go out

Achilles (*to Agamemnon*) Well?

Agamemnon It'll never work. Not in a hundred years.

Odysseus Oh, I don't know, Agamemnon. I like it.

Agamemnon You would! No, Achilles, take my word for it. No wooden horse will ever capture Troy ...

A spotlight holds the model while all the rest of the Lights go down. Thybius comes into the lights and picks up the horse

Thybius The surprising thing was that it did. After ten long years of blood and death, the walls of Troy were finally breached, thanks to this little beauty.

Thunder. Smoke drifts across the stage. The sound of toppling buildings, screams, the shouts of fighting men and the cries of fleeing women. The ground seems to shake, the walls of the city to tremble. Flames are projected across the acting area. The Girls of the Chorus scatter like refugees. The Boys rampage through the town, looting and murdering. Above the uproar we hear the crazed voice of Hecuba

Hecuba (*demented with grief*) I am Hecuba, widow of Troy's king. O, you weeping mothers, weep with me while our city burns.

Polydora Speak to me, Hecuba! Terrors come so thick and fast, I don't know where to run.

Hermione Will they kill us? Every one of us, will they?

Macaria If not, where shall they send us?

Hecuba My children, how shall I know? I ran here, because mad with sick horror I could not stay indoors. Cassandra? Go one of you, bring my daughter to me.

Cassandra, like a sad Ophelia, has wandered on. She wears a long white robe, but under that is as naked as the Arab boy. She also is bedecked with ornaments of every kind, with beads and shells, pebbles, pieces of metal and bone. One of the Girls fetches her

Thybius This is Cassandra, daughter of the Trojan queen. A prophetess in her own right, but cursed by Apollo whose advances she has scorned, never to have her prophecies believed. Oh, unhappy princess ...

Cassandra Mother, is it you?

Hecuba (*embracing her*) Weep, my child, let the tears run. There is no more to be gained by Trojan discipline. Talthybius, hated herald of a hated king, why do you come to mock us?

Thybius Lady, I come with messages from the victorious Greeks.

Althaea What will they do with us? Will they kill us?

Thybius All must go. Some as wives and some as slaves. You, proud Queen, must go with Odysseus. Your daughter——

Hecuba Not Cassandra, no!

Thybius —is claimed by Agamemnon. I must take her to him.

Cassandra Do not weep, Mother, instead put a garland round my head. Do we not hate him? Then I will bring this hated king his death. O, cursed Greek, your cursed life will end in a cursed grave ... and me too they'll fling beside you naked. Oh, Mother, now I foresee my own death! Must I go with him to Argos?

Thybius Not as his slave, lady, but as his second wife. Come, his ships are waiting.

Cassandra I think I see me drowning in the blood of Atreus.

The Soldiers tear her from Hecuba's arms. Thybius takes her out

Hecuba O, great gods, how much more must I live to see?

Soldiers Out, out, dogs, to your masters' ships!

Hecuba Now comes the end. Step proudly, my children. Let us go like Trojans to our death.

The music crashes. The Soldiers drive them out. Five times the gongs and drums strike. Then silence. The flames slowly die. A single pastoral note, high-pitched and trembling. Dawn comes to Argos. As the light builds through dawn to day, three Girls speak

SCENE 4

The Plot

Girl 1 Faster than on eagle's wing, the news is carried——

Girl 2 —that Troy has fallen. From beacon lit on mountain top to mountain top——

Girl 3 —from Ida to Hermes' crag on Lemnos——

Girl 1 —thence to Athos, rock of Zeus.

Girl 2 Crossing the Aegean in a stride——

Girl 3 —to Makistos' heights. Thence to the Messapian Plains——

Girl 1 —and Cithaeron. To the Saronic Gulf——

Girl 2 —and here to Argos where the news is seen by a sleepy watchman . . . on a tower.

Watchman (*on the tower*; *rubbing his eyes*) The signal, the signal I see the signal. Troy has fallen! Ho, wake the Queen! O, welcome, beacon, welcome. You'll set them dancing in the streets of Argos. (*Scrambling down the tower*) Now heaven bring Agamemnon home. May I soon hold his dear hand in mine. Ten years is far too long for any man to be away. (*To the Girls*) Have you heard the news?

They embrace as the Chorus returns

All (*variations of*) Have you heard the news? Is it true Troy has fallen? Will the soldiers be returning now? When will they be here? *etc.*

They break up into groups. Some talk and dance, others prepare sacrifices at the altar, casting incense on the flames. The sun climbs higher into the sky. Now they all join hands and dance in a large circle, much as the Greeks do now. Some wear bells on their ankles and wrists. The mood is light and lyrical

Boy They are preparing the harbour for the return of the ships. They say the army will be home in five days, a week at the most!

A general rush to the entrances clears the arena

Orestes enters with the nurse Cilissa. He is dressed for a journey. He wears a rough hessian coat, a conical straw hat at his back and carries a staff and a bundle. He looks like a shepherd

Cilissa Oh, my dove, my little fish—for you are more mine than hers—my dearest Orestes, let me kiss you once again before you leave. Have you enough food and your extra coat? Oh, when will I see you again?

Orestes (*roughly*) Enough of this fussing, Cilissa, I'm not a child anymore. Look after Electra for me, that's all I ask. I don't like leaving her here by herself and that's for sure.

Cilissa I'll see no harm comes to her. Go well, go well, young one.

Orestes Stay well, stay well, dear Cilissa. (*He hugs her for the last time*) I think I am afraid, but I don't know why.

He goes

Cilissa Bless his heart, I reared him, held him in my arms, and, oh, the times he shouted at me in the night. Made me get up to fetch him a drink of water or a biscuit when he felt hungry. Oh, the dear boy, my dear son— for he is mine, more than his mother's, *that woman*—oh, yes, Agamemnon, I brought up your son for you. Farewell, farewell . . .

She turns back to the Palace. Electra has been watching her

Electra So it *was* my brother? Dearest nurse, dearest Cilissa, where's Orestes going?

Cilissa (*alarmed*) Hush, child, you weren't supposed to know.

Electra But am I not Electra, his own sister?

Cilissa Your mother's orders. He's gone to join his young friend Pylades in Phocis for his education.

Electra But why? And why the secrecy?

Cilissa Don't ask me. No sooner had the news arrived this morning of strong-armed Agamemnon's victory, than she could not get Orestes out of the house quick enough. "Some food for the journey, nurse, and don't worry about his extra shirts. His uncle and I've agreed he's to go at once."

Electra Uncle, indeed! Well, his days are numbered, with my father's return. But why should he want Orestes sent away?

Cilissa I shouldn't ask too many questions, if I were you. You know what they say, least said, soonest mended.

Electra Farewell, Orestes. When shall we meet again, I wonder?

The others return with a rush and great excitement

All (*variation of*) Five days, five days, no more! I can't wait to see my father, I wonder if he'll know me. My husband will be surprised to see the new house. So much has happened in ten years. *etc.*

Guards strike their spears on the ground. Consternation. The Townspeople fall to their knees and cover their faces

All The Queen, the Queen! Cover your faces.

Macaria Now see the change that has come to Argos.
Althaea Terror stalks these streets, lives in each eye.
Boy 1 Men die. Some disappear without trial, without warning.
Alcmene Some fear Aegisthus more than the Queen.
Boy 2 Others hate her most!

*Clytemnestra, taller now, thinner, with face decorated more viciously, enters
with Aegisthus. He also looks more dangerous, a hungry wolf. They both wear
buskins to give them greater formal authority*

Boy 3 He didn't even go to Troy, the pisspot coward.
Boy 4 Shut up!

Silence

Clytemnestra So you've heard? Yes, they're coming home. In five days your
men will be restored to you. Of course we're very proud of them.
Sacrifices must be made, thanks given, all that kind of thing. And your
King will be coming home too. Dear Agamemnon with his long-
shadowed spear and sun-dappled sword, he'll be there also. We must
make sure all is prepared for them. (*She bares her teeth; it is hardly a
smile*) Now to today and these past years. Rumours reach us of a
discontent in the town. It's true that men have disappeared, some have
died without trial. One or two have leapt from the top balconies of the
Palace rather than undergo interrogation. Others have been banished or
confined to their houses and allowed to starve ... Some children have
been put to the sword, malcontents, trouble-makers. Rest assured it was
for the common good. Was there not a war on? Is the home front not as
important to the overall victory as the general with his coming? Your
King is bringing a new concubine I'm told—one of those Trojan
prophetesses, all doom and gloom—well, we'll know how to deal with
her. Be prepared for more changes, that's all I want to say. Go to your
houses now. The curfew will be starting early today, at noon in fact. So
disperse, go on, go quickly and without a sound. You must show the King
you know how to behave.

She turns and leaves with Aegisthus

Alcmene (*turning to her neighbour*) What did she mean? I didn't like the
sound of that.
Guard Silence! Go to your homes! Didn't you hear the Queen?

The Crowd scatters. Only the Chorus remains

Melita A short day, sunrise to noon.
Hiera Outside the empty streets lie naked to the sun.
Leucippe Nothing stirs. Not a dog, not a mule, not a sheep. The olives stand
untended in the midday heat.
Polydora Nothing stirs. Even in the houses we nestle up like little mice
wondering what the cat in the Palace is up to. Five days ...

The sun has passed across. Early afternoon

Hermione Will Agamemnon release us from this terror?
Macaria Hush! You must not speak of it like that.
Boy 1 The Oracle said it. The Oracle meant it. Blood will follow blood. I
was there that day ten years ago. I heard her.
Boy 2 But who will kill who? And will we be better off?

The sun begins to fade. Late afternoon. After another long pause

Boy 3 Rest assured, if anybody benefits, it won't be us. Those that have the
power keep it. The rest of us never have a look in.
in.
Boy 1 Be silent. That is treachery!

Another long pause. Twilight begins

Boy 4 My father was one of those who died by falling from a window. They
say he committed suicide, but I know he was murdered.
Althaea (*gently*) Hush ...

And deepens

Alcmene Hush ...
Melita It cannot last forever.

Another long pause

Heira Or can it?

The last light fades swiftly to black-out

SCENE 5

The Murder

*In the dark a long wailing blast like a ram's horn. Almost the whole of this
scene is ritual. Just as the death of Iphigenia had a North African flavour, this
should have the restrained and formalistic inevitability of the Kabuki. Even the
vocal delivery should contain elements of that almost strangulated, high-
pitched form of oration known as* aragato. *Apart from the Electra scene,
nearly all should be played with long pauses, ritualized gesture and formal
movement giving it a dreamlike atmosphere*

*The Lights come up slowly. A long purple cloth is being unrolled right across
the arena, stretching from the door of the Palace almost to the point where
Agamemnon will enter. Once it is laid nobody must step on it. The Chorus and
Townspeople take up their positions silently, kneeling upright (in the Japanese
manner) on either side of the cloth*

Calchas enters. All bow low

Calchas (*aragato*) The day ... the day is here.

Gong

(*Ditto*) The day dawns ...

He claps his hands and all remain absolutely still, bowing low. Cilissa catches sight of Electra watching from the Palace entrance. She rises and runs to her alarmed

Cilissa What are you doing here? For the god's sake, go!
Electra I've come to greet my father.
Cilissa You know your mother forbade it. Oh, Electra, my child, be gone, be gone. (*Ushering her away*) You know today is all ceremony. The family reunion will be later.

Electra runs out of one entrance as Clytemnestra and her Guard enter from the Palace. Once again Clytemnestra is on buskins. Aegisthus lingers in the background

At the same time Agamemnon and his party including Thybius and Cassandra come in from the other side. Like the Queen, Agamemnon wears a ceremonial mask or robes with immense shoulders as well as the artificial shoes. Separated by the purple carpet they face each other like giant chess pieces

Cilissa runs back to her place. Calchas claps his hands. The Townspeople lift their heads. Calchas bows ritualistically to the Queen, carries his staff to her which she touches, then takes it to the King who in turn touches it; returns to the centre. He lifts it to heaven to be blessed, kneels, bows low three times, sits up on his heels, strikes it on the stage and bows once more to Clytemnestra

Clytemnestra Welcome, great King of Argos.
Calchas (*aragato*) Welcome . . .
Clytemnestra Thrice welcome. Three times we heard of your death in Troy. Three times grieved, three times rejoiced to hear that rumour lied.

All bow. A heavy gong. Calchas bows low once more, sits up on his heels again, strikes the stage with his staff and this time bows to Agamemnon

Agamemnon We thank you, great Queen, for your words and in turn welcome you to our side.
Calchas (*aragato*) Welcome . . .
Agamemnon Thrice welcome, being once for each time you felt yourself bereft of our presence.

The heavy gong

Clytemnestra There is no dearer sight than shelter after storm, no rest better than that after great endurance. Set foot on the pathway like honour at your feet.
Agamemnon (*to Thybius; disconcerted*) What's she talking about? That's not part of the ceremony.
Thybius I think she seeks to do you honour.
Agamemnon Nonsense. She knows I can't set foot on the purple, the gods would never forgive me. (*To Clytemnestra*) Madame, I pray you to excuse me. To set foot on the purple would be to stir great Zeus to jealousy.
Clytemnestra Sire, I beg you.
Agamemnon (*aside*) Damn the woman, she knows purple is the colour of reverence. Madame, to walk on the purple is to hoist myself to the position of a god.

Clytemnestra So you are. God, God Agamemnon!

An intake of horror from all including Calchas who turns to glare balefully at the Queen. Clytemnestra recovers herself

  In his loving wife's eyes.

Agamemnon What does the Priest say?

Calchas He says … (*Aragato*) Imagine Troy had been the victor. What would King Priam have done?

Agamemnon Walked on the purple, damned barbarian.

Calchas Then may victor not walk where the defeated would have slunk?

Agamemnon I'm glad to say I've more humility than Priam.

Clytemnestra (*impatiently*) Oh, humility! This one time, yield, my lord! You've had your conquest, now give me my victory.

Agamemnon Oh, well, if you put it like that. (*He steps off the buskins and prepares to walk barefooted. To Thybius*) Meet me on the other side. And take care of Cassandra. I'll send for her when all this is over. And don't forget she's a prophetess and sacred.

Cassandra (*a terrifying cry*) Owwww! Beware, King! To step on the purple will bring you the hatred of the gods!

Agamemnon I must. My wife is set on it.

He steps on the carpet. Thybius runs to the other end with his buskins. Agamemnon walks slowly to the Queen. A sigh of apprehension from the Townspeople

Clytemnestra (*letting out a roar of triumph*) Eleleleleu! See where the man walks the purple like a god.

The music takes up the cry. Agamemnon reaches the other end, steps on to his buskins which Thybius fastens, as he says

Agamemnon Beloved wife, I have done as you asked.

Clytemnestra Now, Zeus, Fulfiller, fulfil those prayers I made, and *do what must be done.*

The Attendants lift the cloth and carry it behind the royal couple like a train as they walk slowly round the arena. Calchas goes before, cleaning the air and ground with ritual gestures. The Lights are slowly going red, the music sounds more ominous. A distant rumbling is heard

Macaria What is this fear that haunts me?

Althaea A trembling in the air.

Alcmene What does the Queen intend? Has she forgotten Iphigenia?

Melita She made a curse once and yet she smiles and smiles. She will have not forgotten.

The rumbling grows louder. A thin wind slips through the music making everybody shiver

Clytemnestra Come, great King, you must be cleansed of the blood you spilled at Troy. All must be dedicated to the god. I shall perform the purification myself.

Agamemnon Lady, I thank you and for this welcome.

They go out. The Crowd starts to disperse, but the Chorus return to their places around the arena

Boy 1 Something is wrong but I can't put my finger on it.

Boy 2 Look at the Trojan tart. See how she trembles.

Cassandra (*a cry*) O Apollo! O Earth! O horror and death. Blood, I see blood!

Hiera It's blasphemy for her to call on Apollo!

Boy 3 (*to Cassandra*) Be quiet, you Oriental slut!

Cassandra Blood, blood. O Apollo, have you brought me all this way just to my death?

Boy 4 Who would kill *her*? She's not important.

Cassandra Treachery, O, shame. A heart obsessed with hate. (*She runs to escape*)

All Be silent, be silent! (*Pursuing her*)

Thybius (*driving them off*) Leave her alone, she's the King's ward.

He takes Cassandra under his protection. They huddle in the dark as the Lights go down until only the central area is lit

Hiera Inside. We must see what happens inside!

The Chorus hurries back to its places

Agamemnon and Clytemnestra enter. They are in the Palace and do not wear their buskins now. The Attendants still follow with the cloth

Clytemnestra Here, here we'll perform the purification.

Chorus Watch, watch ...

Some of the Attendants help the King to strip off his outerwear. Others bring in basins. Clytemnestra washes him down accompanying each gesture with a ritual prayer

Clytemnestra For Aphrodite, daughter of Zeus and Dione ... for Apollo, son of Zeus and Letto ... for Ares, son of Zeus and Here ... for Artemis, daughter of Zeus and Letto ...

She signals to the Attendants to leave. They lay the cloth on the floor and go

Aegisthus, who has barely shown his face in the proceedings, now enters stealthily and gathers up one end of the cloth

Chorus Watch, watch ...

Clytemnestra For Cronos, father of Zeus ... for Demeter, goddess of the harvest and fruitfulness ... (*She herself picks up the other end of the cloth and wraps the King in it for drying*) All these witness the purification for Zeus. There, it is done, my lord.

She turns him slowly as she speaks so that his arms are tightly bound by the cloth

Chorus (*quietly*) Horror, O, horror, now all is plain ...

Clytemnestra steps back. Aegisthus runs around the King with the cloth pinning him even more securely. Clytemnestra produces a dagger. Agamemnon sees it

Agamemnon O, god, what will you do?
Clytemnestra The murder's mine! Witness, Zeus, his overdue death!

She strikes. The Chorus screams in horror. Aegisthus also uses his dagger

Agamemnon Help, help! Treachery! They're murdering the King! Clytemnestra, my wife——
Clytemnestra No wife to you. Wife no longer. (*With each repetition she stabs him*) Widow now, widow, widow, widow.

With each repetition she stabs him

Agamemnon Aegisthus too? You killed my father.
Aegisthus Now I slay son. Now, now, and again now!

They continue to strike. The music rises to a crescendo. Blood spills on to the floor. Still they strike. Screams and shouts from outside and from the Chorus

All (*variations on*) Help, they're murdering the King. Oh, stop them! Treachery!

Agamemnon falls. A shocked silence

Agamemnon (*as he dies*) Remember the blood curse, Clytemnestra. Orestes will avenge me. Remember Orestes . . .
Clytemnestra Die, Argos! . . . Now, one more remains. He's left his bitch behind! (*She seizes a double-headed axe from the tower and screams as she hurls herself across the stage*) Death to the whore Cassandra!

Cassandra steps into the light as Clytemnestra strikes at her with the axe. A crash of sound accompanies the blow. Again silence. The Prophetess falls

Cassandra Mother, Mother Troy, receive thy daughter. The blood curse is not ended, Clytemnestra . . .

Clytemnestra tramples on her

Clytemnestra Down, down, down, down, down! Now receive her, Earth, and no more speak of mothers. (*She drops the axe*) Iphigenia, you are revenged . . . and Argos, I hold you in my fist of iron.

Aegisthus crosses to her. They embrace and kiss passionately. The Lights fade

Black-out

ACT II

The house lights fade. The gong is struck

SCENE 1

The God Commands

Orestes is alone on stage.

Orestes (*Kneeling and addressing the Oracle*) Seven years have passed, Apollo, since my mother sent me away from Argos. In all that time, stories of her villainy increase. What am I to do? I am now a man. Must I seek a man's revenge?

Music. Two lines of Attendants come up the steps carrying leafy branches with which they beat the stage. The Chorus also takes its place

Attendants (*singing*)
>Gaea, Gaea, hear our song,
>Older than these hills and trees—
>At the month's beginning to shine on earth,
>Shalt thou show two horns to mark six days.
>On the seventh, split the crown in two;
>On the fourteenth, turn the face to view.
>(*Spoken*) Apollo, hear this ancient prayer.

Macaria Older even than the Father Zeus.

Althaea Older than time, older than Ishtar, Erech, Tammuz and Ba'al.

Orestes (*ignoring the Attendants*) To avenge a father's death is one thing, but to kill a mother—!

A low rumble of thunder. The Pythoness speaks off, electronically as before

The Pythoness Orestes, son of Agamemnon . . .

Orestes (*prostrating himself*) Mother of us all.

The Pythoness All who do wrong must be punished. That is god-law, immutable, beyond question.

Orestes That I understand. Since assuming heaven after the older gods, Zeus has made his meaning plain. All living things that do wrong must be punished. Nevertheless . . .

The Pythoness Then why your question?

Orestes Great god Apollo and great Oracle through whom the god speaks, consider my position. My mother slew my father, that's the long and short of it. To avenge him, must I then kill her?

The Pythoness enters. The Chorus and Attendants kneel

The Pythoness You have given your answer. Is she not a sinner?

Orestes But to kill my mother! Is that what Apollo really wants?

The Pythoness Shed blood, that is the god's command. The sinners' guilt is world-heavy. They deserve to die.

Orestes By my hand?

The Pythoness Are you not your father's natural avenger?

Orestes But having slain my uncle and ... my mother, where may I turn for pity?

The Pythoness (*quickly*) Not here, that much is clear. Murder for murder, that is the god's command, but he cannot countenance matricide.

Orestes But to kill one's mother *is* matricide!

The Pythoness That's your dilemma. It's an edict going back to the older religion. Ouranos set three sins aside, deserving more punishment than any other; blasphemy, treachery to host or guest, and the spilling of kindred blood. The breaking of any of these, will call down on your head those Furies, named the Happy Ones, whose ancestors come from the depths of time. They'll tear your flesh from bone, and even bone from bone, if you offend them.

Orestes But my mother's sin—why did they not punish her? She shed my father's blood!

The Pythoness Being wife not sister, it was not kindred.

Orestes Then my so-called uncle, my father's cousin, did he not spill kindred blood?

The Pythoness Too far removed. You have our answer. Revenge the murders you must, but in doing so you'll incur the wrath of the old religion.

Chorus Beware the Eumenides, Orestes. Beware, beware!

The Pythoness starts to leave. The Attendants rise and sing their verse again, beating time with their branches as Orestes cries out in agony

Orestes O, great seer of the god, stay! At least offer me some protection for this thing I must do!

The Pythoness has gone. The Attendants follow her out slowly

A long pause

Orestes (*calling out sadly*) Pylades?

Pylades (*entering*) I am here. Did the god speak?

Orestes (*a nod*) I must do the deed but evermore remain accountable for it.

Pylades Then you must do it.

Orestes Oh, god, I see this line of blood stretching backwards to the beginning of time and forwards again till the ending of the world. When will it ever cease?

Pylades Perhaps with you. Come, put on the harness of necessity. I will return with you to Argos, there to begin your revenge.

The big gong sounds five times

SCENE 2

The Return

Argos. The Lights go green. A buzzing of flies. The Eumenides gather in clusters, old women with vicious faces, or masks, half-concealed by veils. The Chorus speaks

Alcmene Now comes vengeance!

Melita And all Argos—green as putrescent flesh—swells and seeks relief. Here a great King lived——

Hiera —and died. And the murderers still sit on the blood-stained throne.

Leucippe Help us, Orestes, bring us peace!

Polydora Give us hope.

Hermione We're such little people and quite unable to take sides like you.

The Eumenides buzz restlessly

Boy 1 The whole place stinks of death, excrement and vomit.

Boy 2 (*swatting flies*) The flies are as big as birds and treat us as equals——

Boy 3 (*also swatting*) —worse. They grab the rotting food from our rotting mouths, the bastards.

Boy 4 Oh, do get a move on, Orestes. Come and revenge us or we'll all die of doing nothing.

Thybius (*stepping forward*) Yes, seven years have passed since Orestes left Argos for Phocia. Now he has grown from childhood to maturity. Remember that when you wonder why nobody recognizes him when he returns home. We have just the one actor, but think of him before as just a boy, all for flying kites and fishing with a bent pin, but see him now as a man with his heart set on murder. To show how much he'd changed and why nobody knew him, he and Pylades will wear masks to help the deception. Here they come now.

The rumble of distant thunder. A cold wind rises. All shiver and cover their faces

Winter. The wind raises grains of dust that cut the face like glass ... A cheerless time.

Orestes (*after a long pause, looking round*) Is this really Argos ... the town where I was born? This loathsome heap of offal blowing in the wind. (*To Boy 1*) Is it?

Boy 1 (*spitting*) What of it?

Orestes Argos?

Thybius (*pleased*) See, nobody knows him. Keep it like that.

Boy 2 (*whining*) Alms, master?

Boy 3 Some food?

Boy 4 A little money?

They rise and move about as cripples, diseased and deformed

Orestes (*horrified*) The whole place is inhabited by beggars!

Pylades They say nobody cares anymore. In any case, how much work can you do when the curfew allows you into the fields for only one hour a day?

Orestes But we were such a proud people!
Chorus Alms, alms for the love of Zeus.

They set up a general clamour. Out of it the music builds and a chant is heard. Orestes and Pylades hide in the dark. Electra, wearing rags and looking twice her age, leads a Procession to Agamemnon's grave, carrying bowls of flowers and wine on their heads, for offering

All   Year in, year out,
                                We come this way,
                                Bearing gifts
                                To Agamemnon's grave.
                                Here he lies,
                                Poor body of a murdered King.
                                Peace to Agamemnon,
                                Peace to his shade we sing.

Electra Great Father, seven years to the day, we attend your grave—this unmarked heap of stones where your body was flung to lie with dead dogs, pigs and the city's dung—to honour you. But truth to tell we have so little honour left, even our words sound empty now.
Orestes It's Electra, my sister!

Pylades stops him rushing to her

Electra Once we used to reverence the royal line, even the gods. Now all is turned to apathy and despair.
Macaria Argos is a city of the damned.
Althaea Dance, Electra, dance for your father.

The Chorus sets up a beat by making gasping noises, slow at first, but soon quickening in tempo. Electra begins to dance. As she does so, the Chorus and Electra herself cry out lines—not like the wailing in the Iphigenia scene, but abruptly, bluntly—as if they were part of the ritual

Alcmene One day, one day you'll see, Orestes will come!
Melita Great Orestes to avenge the deed.
Boy 1 Carrying his father's sword——
Boy 2 —and his long-shadowed spear.
Electra Orestes, great Orestes! Come, my brother, come!
Boy 3 Striding over the hill, his hair blowing over his eyes——
Electra Come, my brother, come!
Hiera —his shoulders set back like a soldier's——
Electra (*panting*) Come, my brother, come!
Leucippe —his proud feet printing the earth——
Electra Come, my brother, come! (*Suddenly she breaks off the dance and flings herself on the ground*)
All (*variations of*) What's wrong, Electra? What have you found? Why has she stopped? *etc.*
Electra (*pointing*) Somebody has been here! Whose footprint is this?
All (*variations of*) There were two strangers. Two men. We hadn't seen them before. Where did they go? Did anybody see them? *etc.*
Electra Two strangers?

She stands and looks directly at the place where Orestes and Pylades are hiding. They come forward slowly. Electra tears her eyes away to measure her foot against the print on the ground. Then she looks at them again

Electra Can it be?
Chorus Can it be?
Electra How shall I know him?
Chorus How? How? How?

Cilissa runs forward

Cilissa He had a scar, caused when you and he were chasing a fawn. His foot caught on a stone and another scored his head just—(*she touches Orestes' brow*)—there. (*Very softly*) Lady and my child, it is he.

A wild ululation. Electra and Orestes stare at each other for a moment and then fall into each other's arms like lovers. Cilissa and Pylades are also embraced

All (*variations of*) It is he! The day has come! *etc.*

The savage rejoicing continues. Noise, stamping, dancing, drumming on the floor. It ends abruptly as Orestes draws his sword. Silence and stillness

Orestes Lead me to my revenge.

The music and drumming start again. Orestes and Pylades are led off by Electra and some of the Townspeople

The Eumenides call out to one another

Remorse The day, the day is come, my sisters.
Guilt But we must still bide our time.
Remorse As watchdogs of the old religion, we will make his life a misery, gnaw at his conscience, chew at his resolution. Our aim—to drive him to suicide through remorse.
Guilt But only after he has committed the crime.
Remorse Of course, of course.
Shame He may change his mind.
Regret Not he, his arms are steeped in blood.
Guilt As far as the feud with Aegisthus goes, certainly. But remember, that doesn't concern us. We are here to do Ouranos' bidding. Only the spilling of the kindred blood—his mother's—interests us. Until then, stay watching . . .

They split up but remain in the auditorium hissing malevolently from time to time, Thybius and Cilissa step forward

Thybius So seven years to the day since Agamemnon died they were united.
Cilissa Oh, such a happy day. I remember as if it were last week. The thirteenth of January, only we called it Gamelion. Bless their dear hearts.
Thybius Electra took Orestes to her hovel—
Cilissa Oh, she'd had such a bad time of it, my little fish. Banished from the Palace quite early on. Married off to a labourer way beneath her but he did his best.

Thybius There they made their plans. They knew where they would find Aegisthus—working in his fields.

Cilissa It was just like old times with my little doves whispering and nodding—

Thybius Come along, old woman. You can tell them about that another time.

They go off, Cilissa telling Thybius all about it in mime. Five beats of the drum

SCENE 3

The Revenge

A single high-pitched note of music. The very air seems to be standing tip-toe with anticipation. Aegisthus is clearing stones and weeds from his fields. Every now and again he mimes throwing the stones in the direction of Agamemnon's grave. Orestes and Pylades enter and watch him quietly. Aegisthus straightens up and sees them

Aegisthus Greetings, strangers. Who are you and where do you come from?

A long pause

Orestes Thessalians. We journey to sacrifice to Olympian Zeus.

Aegisthus Stay here today and be my guests.

A long pause. Orestes and Pylades exchange a look

Pylades Gladly.

Aegisthus I'm killing a bull today in honour of the Nymph, so there'll be plenty to eat. (*He goes back to work*)

They watch for a long time. At length

Orestes Tell me, why do you throw all your stones on to that grave there?

Aegisthus (*a laugh*) Oh, that? It's an old habit of mine. An old beggar's body was once thrown there—one we called Agamemnon. Now I've got into the way of throwing all my rubbish there. As I do, I utter a little prayer, nothing special, just something of my own.

A pause. He goes back to work. They watch. At length

Pylades Tell us what you say?

Aegisthus I say—(*throwing stones and sneering*)—"Come, Orestes, come and claim your own."

Pylades glances quickly at Orestes. The latter brings his sword out from under his cloak. Aegisthus bends to collect more stones

Macaria Now, Orestes, strike!

Orestes Who is Orestes?

Aegisthus Another madman who used to live hereabouts.

Orestes (*a shout*) Then has he come to claim his inheritance!

Chorus (*loudly*) Now!

Orestes strikes as Aegisthus is straightening up. The blow catches the victim on the back of the head. Aegisthus falls to his knees, catches sight of his attacker's face

Aegisthus Orestes ...?

Orestes strikes again

Althaea (*screaming*) O, Zeus, no! What have we done!
Others Stop him, stop him!

Aegisthus crumples up. Pylades drags the body into the dark and throws his cloak over it. Orestes stands motionless. Then he turns abruptly

Alcmene It's too late. His heart is set on murdering his mother.
Melita Keep a strong heart, Orestes, when the moment comes to slay her.
Hiera What can I say? She is his mother. Poor, misguided woman at whose breast the infant murderer fed——
Leucippe —she killed her husband!
Polydora But to slay a mother is the most terrible crime of all!
Hermione Perhaps he will not do it, perhaps, perhaps!

Orestes walks to the Palace entrance and kneels. Now the tempo quickens. We hear three resounding metallic blows as if Orestes has struck the bronze door of the Palace. One of the Boys runs forward and mimes the act of pushing back the giant door. Clytemnestra steps forward

Clytemnestra Who is it? Who is it that knocks?
Orestes A traveller, one who has news for you. On my way here, a man—I know not whom he was—asked me to deliver this message to the Queen. "Tell her," he said, "that her son Orestes is dead."
Clytemnestra Dead? O, ye gods, is this true? I don't know whether to rejoice or grieve. Come, come, young man, into the Palace and tell me all you know.

He rises and follows. She leads him round the arena and into an inner circle of light. The Chorus close in, hemming them in, and the Eumenides prepare to move

Remorse Now, my sisters, the moment approaches.
Guilt The deed, we must wait for the deed!
Orestes I only wish I could have brought you better news.
Clytemnestra You shall be made as welcome as if you had.

A wind starts blowing. A Voice can be heard shouting from far away

Voice Treachery! The King Aegisthus has been slain by the stranger from another land.
Clytemnestra What is this? Slain, my husband?
Orestes Yes, madame, first by your hand and then by mine!

He takes off the mask. By now the Chorus and Eumenides have crept so far forward they hardly have room to move

Clytemnestra Orestes! Would you kill your own mother?

Orestes (*drawing his sword*) Did you not kill my father and marry with his cousin? "Look upon this picture and on this—the counterfeit present-ment of two cousins." (*Engravings on either side of the sword blade*) "See what a grace was seated on this brow; Hyperion's curls; the front of Jove himself. Look you now what follows—"

Clytemnestra "O, speak no more, Orestes. Thou turn'st mine eyes into my very soul and there I see such black and grained spots as will not leave their tinct."

The ghost of Agamemnon appears

Agamemnon Kill her!

Orestes O, Zeus, see where he stands!

Clytemnestra "Whereon do you look?"

Orestes "On him, on him!"

Clytemnestra I see no-one.

Agamemnon Kill her!

Orestes Now Zeus give me strength!

He strikes. Red mist pours from the top of the tower. The murder is repeated three times. With each blow, the heaviest drum is struck and the Chorus cries out

Chorus Horror ... horror ... horror!

After the third stroke Clytemnestra clings to the sword then her hands claw their way up Orestes' arm and drag him down to kiss him

Clytemnestra Oh, Orestes, you were my son once. (*She dies*)

A crash of music. A wail from the Chorus

Chorus Oh, terrible death!

Remorse Now, you avengers, strike!

The Eumenides race forward

Eumenides (*screaming*) Vengeance!

Orestes O, Zeus, the Furies! See their pus-laden eyes!

The arrival of the Eumenides has scattered the Chorus. Cries of "treachery! the Queen is dead." "Where is Orestes?" "Zeus save us," *and so on, drive the cast back and forth across the arena*

Pylades fights his way through to Orestes who is cowering from the Furies

Pylades Orestes, come! We'll seek sanctuary in Apollo's temple.

Orestes Electra? I cannot leave Electra!

Pylades She'll come with us!

The wind howls. All double up to fight their way through the storm which rages through the town. The Women draw their veils over their faces

Orestes, Pylades and Electra struggle to the tower and climb it until they are just out of reach of the Furies who strike and claw at them while yelling for revenge

Shame The ancient curse thus for the third time brings a hurricane's havoc on this house of blood!

Orestes (*tormented*) Apollo, O, Apollo, save us!

A crash of thunder. Slowly the uproar dies

The Pythoness (*the electronic voice*) Orestes, Apollo hears.

The Eumenides withdraw slightly, muttering resentfully

The Pythoness Go to Athens, there to stand your trial. Athene herself will hear your case. I, Apollo, will defend you. Back, Furies, back! Orestes is my charge.

The lights change. Peace returns. Orestes and his two companions descend the tower, but the Eumenides remain grouped together, hissing and muttering

SCENE 4

The Trial

Thybius So to Athens for the trial. I myself didn't see this for I was dead by now, but there are many excellent law reports of the proceedings so I can tell you exactly what happened. First twelve Athenians were appointed jurors and then the goddess Athene arrived to try the case. The Eumenides brought the charge—murder most foul, the spilling of a mother's blood—speaking on behalf of the old religion, while Apollo, standing for the new order of morality and reason, defended Orestes.

A fanfare. In the background, birds sing. All is now serenity and light. The court settles to hear the case

Athene This trial raises several interesting points in law. First, what is justice and how does it differ from vengeance? The second, has religion any place in justice? And third, to see, if only by the way, the status of women in marriage. For whereas the accused claims he killed his mother for what she'd done, no person has asked to speak in defence of Clytemnestra. This interests me, for as a woman, albeit a goddess, I believe that if anybody took it upon herself to prove the Queen was right to kill her husband, Orestes would automatically be placed in the wrong! However, nobody doing so, we must assume there is no justice for wives ... yet. (*To the Eumenides*) Since you are the accusers, speak.

Remorse First, did you kill your mother?

Orestes I cannot deny it.

Regret Good, the first round is ours.

Remorse How?

Orestes With a sword.

Guilt On whose advice?

Orestes Apollo's.

Shame Tell us what he said.

Apollo Objection. I am Apollo and will speak for myself. Reported speech by the accused will only be hearsay evidence.

Athene Objection over-ruled. What the prosecution is seeking to ascertain is not what you said, but what the accused *thought* you said.

Remorse Oh, wise and upright judge, how I do honour thee.

Guilt (*to Orestes*) So tell us.

Orestes He told me to commit the crime.

Shame The son of Zeus commanded matricide?

Orestes He did, in his temple at Delphi.

Regret I find that difficult to believe.

Apollo If I may interrupt, m'lady, my testimony will confirm that what the accused says is in essence correct.

Athene Thank you, Apollo. (*To the Eumenides*) Please, continue.

A set-back for the Prosecution. Mutter, mutter. They try another tack

Remorse Why did you seek the god's advice?

Orestes My mother had twice offended.

Guilt Twice?

Orestes She'd killed a husband and a father.

Shame We must protest, learned goddess. The accused is seeking to complicate the issue!

Athene Not at all, it's a perfectly valid point of law. Indeed, I wouldn't blame him if he claimed she'd also killed a *king*. That would make the balance on his side overwhelming.

Apollo Oh, wise and upright judge, how I do honour thee.

Athene For then he'd have three reasons for seeking the god's help. The Olympian law quite clearly states that a wrong-doer must be punished. Therefore a triple murderer——

Eumenides Objection, objection!

Remorse We must protest, m'lady! This is the first we've heard that this case is to be tried by Olympian law. We were told quite firmly—my friends and I—that it would be heard under Ouranian law which states categorically that spilling kindred blood is—*de facto*—unpardonable.

Support from the Eumenides and their party

Athene Yes, that's true. I hadn't considered that.

Disappointment from Orestes' side

Macaria O, Zeus, see how Orestes pales. The goddess tried to help him——

Althaea —but is now trapped by her own sense of justice.

Apollo (*rather pompously*) Merciful goddess, may I speak? You indicated at the beginning of the trial this case would examine how justice differs from vengeance.

Guilt We're not interested in that. We seek vengeance!

Apollo And we seek justice. Now it seems to me——

Eumenides Objection! Objection!

Apollo —that fairness is the keystone of all justice. The accused did not kill blindly. He sought advice of every kind and then made up his mind accordingly. If he'd struck in rage, I'd concede the prosecution's point, but like it or not, this is a case of justice, for balancing reason against reason and act against act, he committed *a thinking man's crime*.

Shame Nevertheless he must be punished!

Apollo Of course, but what sort of punishment?

Athene How say you? Death?

Eumenides Yes! Yes!

Regret By remorse. Suicide.

Eumenides Yes, suicide!

Athene What do you say, Orestes?

Orestes You'll get no remorse from me.

Remorse We will, by the time we've finished with you, my beauty.

Orestes Nor do I feel guilt.

Apollo Which is exactly my point. Vengeance is blind. Justice invokes reason. Kill Orestes if you can, but you'll never get him to kill himself. As a modern man, he knows himself to be innocent.

Eumenides Guilty! Guilty! Guilty!

Apollo For what is guilt but a state of mind. Condemn him all you like, but until he feels guilty, believes himself to be guilty, knows himself to be guilty, all the punishment in the world will be completely pointless.

Uproar. The Cast takes sides, yelling "Guilty" or "Innocent" according to their beliefs. Athene calls for silence

Thybius The argument raged this way and that. It was, you see, a conflict between the old gods and the new, between blind emotion and reason. Difficult for Athene because she, like Apollo, belonged to the new order.

Athene Let us take a vote. Jurors, you have heard the issues. What it boils down to is this: Orestes has admitted that he committed the murders, but was he justified or not? That's the answer you must give us.

Each Juror has a black pebble and a white one. In turn they go to the urn and drop one or the other in—white for "innocent", black for "guilty"

Remorse I still protest! The court's making a mockery of the law!

Athene Let the votes be counted. If Orestes is acquitted he'll go free. If not, he'll be handed over to the Furies for punishment.

Macaria Now we'll see.

Guilt Now! Now!

Shame Ouranos, don't cheat me! I'll tear the lids off his eyes.

Regret The tenderest parts of the soles of his feet are for me.

Remorse His tongue is mine!

Electra Oh, my brother, hold me tight. If they rip you piece by piece, let them take me also.

Pylades And I. Beyond death even as in life.

Athene Have you counted the votes?

Boy 1 We have.

Athene And what's the answer?

Boy 2 Six of one and half-a-dozen of the other.

Eumenides He's ours, he's ours!

Chorus No, ours!

Athene holds up her hand

Athene This calls for a casting vote. I say Orestes is free ... on one
condition.

Orestes Speak it!

Athene Agree with what Apollo says. Go forth feeling no guilt. But suffer
one ounce of remorse, the tiniest twinge of conscience, and the Furies will
strip you limb from limb.

Orestes So be it.

Thybius And that was their verdict.

*Uproar. The Eumenides howl their protest. We can barely hear the fanfare
that signals the departure of Apollo and Athene. The Chorus and others
congratulate Orestes and then run to their places for the next scene*

Macaria So he set out, half-free, half-shackled, knowing that every step of
the way he'd be followed by the Eumenides.

Althaea One drop of regret and he'd be lost!

Alcmene What a difficult thing is shame. Or regret or sorrow. How can you
prevent yourself, even in sleep, murmuring just once, "Mother, I am
sorry"?

Melita Just to form his lips in the shape of that one repentent word
"mother" and the Furies would have him.

Hiera "Mother, I am sorry." How many times haven't I said it?

Leucippe And I.

Polydora And I.

Hermione Sometimes without a thought.

Boy 1 I don't often say it, but I think it occasionally.

Macaria And even that would have been his downfall—just to *think* it!

Boy 2 In the still of the night—

Boy 3 Or listening to some music—

Boy 4 Or remembering some little scene from his childhood, how could he
not think it?

Boy 5 "Mother, I am sorry."

Thybius He'd already spent a year seeking sanctuary and purification from
anybody who offered it. Now he returned to Apollo's temple at Delphi,
weary and sick at heart. It seemed to him that the load Athene had given
him was more than anyone could bear. Remember, he couldn't even feel
doubt!

SCENE 5

The Fulfilment

*The Lights narrow down. Orestes falls to his knees. The Eumenides circle him
silently and then climb the tower, clinging there in clusters like bats*

Remorse It won't be long now. See, he is weakening.

Orestes Mother ...

Shame There!

Guilt Wait!
Orestes Mother of us all . . .
Guilt He calls the Oracle.
Orestes Tell me what to do.

The Lights reveal The Pythoness already standing veiled nearby, but the voice—as always—echoes electronically

The Pythoness What do you seek?
Orestes Peace. My feet have felt every road in Greece. Sometimes I move not only every day but several times during the night as well. No place sees me more than once, but everywhere I go the Furies hound me. Put out a hand to steady myself, they are there. Blink an eye, they are there. Kneel to pray and they are there, and there, and there. Is this what Athene meant? Will it continue to the day I die, without peace, without rest?
The Pythoness Where are Electra and Pylades?
Orestes Beyond the grove, waiting.
The Pythoness They must marry. Apollo commands it.
Orestes It shall be done. But for me?
The Pythoness There is a little northern town beyond the Bosphorus and across the Black Sea called Tauris. The people of this land have a wooden image of Artemis in their temple which reached them by ill-chance. If you were to steal that image and return it to the goddess's temple at Athens, who is to say you would not find rest?
Orestes Artemis? She has no reason to love me. Didn't she send the winds against my father when he was trying to sail for Troy? Didn't she demand the sacrifice of my little sister Iphigenia which drove my mother mad and caused all this blood to flow?
The Pythoness I have spoken.
Orestes No, no, this is another trap. The gods are tricking me again! (*He rises not a little mad with weariness and suffering*)
The Pythoness Do you question me?
Orestes Yes and again, yes! I'm weary of these games that taunt men and drive them wild with pain.
The Pythoness Orestes!
Orestes No more, I say, no more!

He draws his sword and drives it through The Pythoness. The Chorus cries out in horror. The figure collapses—the costume is empty

A long pause

Even Orestes is overcome by fear for what he has done. And then the electronic voice speaks again

The Pythoness Poor child, do you really think you can kill the gods? Is it remorse that drives you to these lengths?
Orestes For my mother? No!
The Pythoness But you still seek absolution?
Orestes So much, so much . . .
The Pythoness Then go to Tauris. Perhaps you'll find it there.

Orestes heaves himself up with much sighing. The music starts, accompanying the action. Orestes and Pylades say farewell to Electra and then set off on their journey, trudging round and round the arena, falling over rocks, scaling mountains, jumping crevasses, swimming rivers, growing wearier and wearier. (The actual incidents can be developed during improvisations with the cast.) Music is heard in the background during the following exchange

Girl 1 So off they set for the North. It was much the same route as the message had come signalling Troy's downfall, ten years before.

Girl 2 Only in reverse. From the Saronic Gulf to Cithaeron——

Girl 3 —thence to the Messapian Plains and Makistos' heights——

Girl 1 —and so on and so on.

Boy 4 (*to his neighbour*) Only girls in this bit. I'm going to have a kip. (*This line would depend on the number of boys used in this final scene*)

Girl 3 Across the Aegean, not in a stride but in a ship—

Orestes and Pylades row and row and sadly scan the horizon for signs of land

Girl 2 To the Bosphorus and so to the Black Sea and the little town called Tauris. Here they were to steal the image of Artemis which the gods desired.

Girl 1 What they did not know was that Tauris was ruled by an evil king who made sacrifices of all travellers who came to the land.

Orestes and Pylades beach their boat and hide it. And then they hide themselves while surveying their situation. They are both tired and afraid. The former, in particular, is anxious in case the Furies have followed them

Girl 3 One other thing they did not know. The statue of Artemis was looked after by a priestess they were to recognize.

While Pylades persuades his friend to sleep, the Lights reveal Iphigenia in prayer before the statue of Artemis together with the Attendants. While the latter remain kneeling

Iphigenia (*to the audience*) I am Iphigenia. Twenty years ago Artemis carried me to this place when my father Agamemnon sought to kill me for the right wind to take his ships to Troy. They tied me to a frame, Calchas raised the knife—I remember my father Agamemnon growing pale—and then all went black. One, two, three seconds, and when I opened my eyes again, here I was. Later Artemis told me how she'd saved my life, leaving in my place only a replica for the priest to find. But why should she do this if not to send me home one day? Yet twenty years have passed and no word has come from Argos. Last night I dreamt my brother Orestes was dead. Can that be a sign that my exile is coming to an end? (*She turns back to the statue*) O, beloved Artemis, give peace to my dear brother and his grieving sister. (*She joins the others in prayer again*)

A brief silence. The Furies enter secretly, see the sleeping travellers and advance on them stealthily. At the last moment Orestes awakes

Orestes (*crying in horror*) O, ye gods, the Furies! Wake, wake, Pylades, they have followed us after all.

Panic. Pylades wakes and defends his friend. Orestes behaves like a man in an epileptic fit, raves, rails and falls down. Iphigenia and the Attendants start to their feet

Iphigenia Who are they? Go some of you and bring those travellers here. They must die as the King commands.

Some of the Attendants, who are armed, run to the travellers

The Furies withdraw

Pylades sees he has no option but to surrender and assists Orestes to approach and kneel before Iphigenia

Iphigenia Who are you and why do you come to this forbidden land?

Pylades explains their journey in mime

Girl 1 While Pylades told the priestess of their journey from the South, she found her attention being drawn more and more to the one who had cried out. When she heard they came from Argos—the very town where she'd been born—her pity knew no bounds for the two young men who must die.

Iphigenia Alas, why did you come? Do you not know we must kill all strangers here?

Orestes O, gods, you have lied again. I knew this was but another trap. Sweet priestess, why should we both die? Save my friend, but let me die for both of us.

Iphigenia Would you really have it so?

Orestes Yes! for I have nothing left to live for. I am half-mad with torment and everything I touch turns to blood. Why have I been so cursed? Yes, take my life but spare his. He has been loyal to death and deserves all the rewards the gods can give. Spare him!

Pylades No, no never.

Iphigenia (*raising a commanding hand*) Then that is how it shall be. (*To Pylades*) In return for your life you shall carry a secret message for me to Argos. (*To the Attendants*) Prepare for this man's death. (*To Pylades again*) On pain of death you shall reveal its contents to nobody but the person to whom it is addressed. (*She hands him a small package*)

Pylades But what if it be lost or the ship sinks? Should you not tell me to whom you write and what the letter says?

Iphigenia (*agreeing*) That shall I do. (*To the Attendants of Orestes*) Take this man! (*To Pylades*) The message is too important to be entrusted to parchment alone. It is to my brother Orestes telling him that his sister Iphigenia is alive and needs his help. But if he is dead——

Pylades (*joyfully*) Iphigenia? Then is my mission soon accomplished. (*He takes the letter to Orestes who is being surrounded by the Attendants*) See, here it is delivered.

Iphigenia (*angrily*) What is this? I told you the matter was secret.

Pylades But, lady, this *is* Orestes. O, beloved gods——

Iphigenia He?

Orestes My sister?

Girl 1 Then everything was explained——

Girl 2 —Orestes showed her his scar, talked to her of Electra and of Cilissa, their nurse, proved he was her brother——

Alcmene —telling her even of the death of their father and mother——

During all this, the reunion. Brother and sister embrace, talk, embrace again. The Attendants watch suspiciously

Macaria —and Pylades told her why they'd come—to steal the statue for Artemis.

Iphigenia Now shall I help you, for I am sick of this place of death and irreverence. Seize the statue and take it to your ship, for it seems it is the sign of your redemption. Meet me there. I shall join you shortly.

Orestes and Pylades move out of sight of the Attendants, seize the image and run with it. Immediately there is uproar

Attendants (*variations of*) Help, mistress, they have stolen the holy image. The strangers are escaping. Call the King! *etc.*

Furies (*returning; variations of*) Quick, quick, Orestes is escaping. Stop them! *etc.*

Iphigenia Be still!

The uproar dies

Do you not see the strangers have defiled the image by their action. Summon the King by all means, but first withdraw from this place while I purify them and attend to the purification of the goddess we worship.

Mutter, mutter from all

Enough, be gone. I will only speak the rite in private.

All move off

Now Orestes, I come. Farewell for ever to this place. Dear Artemis, who spared my life once, do so I beseech you, yet again. Bring us safely with your image to Athens.

She joins Orestes and Pylades at their ship, they push it out to sea, clamber aboard and start to row home carrying the image with them. Everybody returns with a rush, protesting loudly

All Save us, save us, Artemis!

A crash of thunder, a howling gale. All on shore fall to their knees, Furies included. The Travellers pull on the oars, the music builds

Orestes Now is it over and I am free at last.

Pylades Row, row for home. Only peace and happiness await us now.

Iphigenia Peace and forgiveness from the gods.

Melita So all was well. Bless the gods!

Hiera And from that day forth, the Furies ceased to trouble Orestes.

Leucippe Praise Apollo. That little town of Tauris had provided the answer, and the image of Artemis was carried safe to Athens.

Joyful music. The whole Cast stands as Orestes carries the image to Artemis'
temple and places it on the altar. Iphigenia and Electra are reunited.
Everybody rejoices as Athene accepts the image for the gods

Thybius Thus ends the legend of Agamemnon. One more murder remained.
Aletes, Aegisthus' son, claimed the kingdom after his father's death, so
Orestes had to kill *him* also, but after that, the blood curse which
accompanied the story came to an end as well. Orestes finally died at the
age of seventy ... of a snake-bite.

Polydora Praise the gods.

Hermione Remember, out of suffering great good *can* come.

Macaria For it is out of suffering that man learns.

All (*singing*)   Go and good go with you,
Rich in Fortune's favour.
When Gods and Fate are reconciled
All lives are crowned with joy!

END

PROPERTY LIST

ACT I

Altar
Tripod with burning incense
Scaffolding tower
Bowl of drugged smoke for **Attendant**
Sacrificial knife for **Priest**
Masks for **Chorus**
Pebbles for **Chorus**
Sacrificial frame for **Iphigenia**
Bowls for **Iphigenia's** blood
White veils for **Clytemnestra**
Basins, towels, cushions, wine flasks for **Agamemnon's** tent
Model of the Wooden Horse, wrapped in a blanket for **Arab Boy**
Staff, bundle for **Orestes**
Spears for **Guards**
Long purple cloth
Staff for **Calchas**
Dagger for **Clytemnestra**
Dagger for **Aegisthus**
Axe for **Clytemnestra**

> *Personal:*   **Iphigenia:** strapped to her side bladder containing blood
> **Agamemnon:** strapped to his side bladder containing blood

ACT II

Altar
Leafy branches for **Attendants**
Bowls of flowers and wine for **Electra** and the **Procession**
Sword for **Orestes**
Black and white pebbles for each **Juror**
Mock figure of the Pythoness
Statue of Artemis
Small package for **Iphigenia**

LIGHTING PLOT

ACT I

Property fittings required: *nil*

To open: General working lighting on stage

Cue 1	The **Girls'** and **Boys'** agony is doubled *Lights go red*	(Page 1)
Cue 2	**Calchas:** "First one and then the other, you shall be told." *Lights change as dawn approaches*	(Page 2)
Cue 3	**Boys:** "Blood ... blood ... blood ... blood ... blood!" *Lights turn green*	(Page 3)
Cue 4	During rapid exchange between **Agamemnon** and **Calchas** *Lights slowly return to normal*	(Page 4)
Cue 5	**All:** "For Troy!" *All lighting goes down except for the spotlight on Thybius*	(Page 6)
Cue 6	**Thybius:** "... where that damned North wind was still blowing." *Sunlight effect*	(Page 6)
Cue 7	The singing and music stop *Black-out for three seconds then return to sunlight effect*	(Page 9)
Cue 8	The **Men** go out *Lights slowly go down until only the central area is seen*	(Page 10)
Cue 9	**Clytemnestra:** "... his very juice of life is drying up." *Single spotlight on Agamemnon*	(Page 10)
Cue 10	**Thybius** comes to **Agamemnon** and calms him *Spotlight slowly fades*	(Page 10)
Cue 11	Fanfare *Lights come up hard and bright*	(Page 13)
Cue 12	**Agamemnon:** "No wooden horse will ever capture Troy." *Spotlight holds the Model, while all the rest of the lights go down*	(Page 16)
Cue 13	A single pastoral note, high pitched and trembling *Lighting builds through dawn to day*	(Page 17)
Cue 14	All ad lib *Increase lighting so the sun appears to climb higher into the sky*	(Page 17)
Cue 15	**Polydora:** "Five days ..." *Lights change to early afternoon effect, as the sun moves across*	(Page 19)
Cue 16	**Boy 2:** "And will we be better off!" *Fade sunlight effect to resemble late afternoon*	(Page 20)

Cue 17   **Boy 1:** "That is treachery!"   (Page 20)
            Lights begin to change to twilight effect

Cue 18   **Althaea:** "Hush . . ."   (Page 20)
            Lights deepen

Cue 19   **Heira:** "Or can it?"   (Page 20)
            The remaining lighting fades swiftly to black-out

Cue 20   A long wailing blast like a ram's horn   (Page 20)
            Lights come up slowly

Cue 21   **Calchas** goes before, cleaning the air and ground with ritual   (Page 22)
            gestures
            Lights slowly go red

Cue 22   **Thybius:** ". . . she's the King's ward."   (Page 23)
            Lights go down until only the central area is lit

Cue 23   **Aegisthus** and **Clytemnestra** embrace and kiss passionately   (Page 24)
            Lights fade to black-out

ACT II

To open: General working lighting on stage

Cue 24   The big gong sounds five times   (Page 27)
            Lights go green and remain so until the end of Scene 2

Cue 25   Beginning of Scene 3   (Page 30)
            Return to general working lighting

Cue 26   **Clytemnestra** leads **Orestes** round the arena   (Page 31)
            Spotlight

Cue 27   **The Pythoness:** "Orestes is my charge."   (Page 33)
            Lights change

Cue 28   Beginning of Scene 5   (Page 36)
            Lights narrow down

Cue 29   **Orestes:** "Tell me what to do."   (Page 37)
            Lighting reveals the Pythoness

Cue 30   While Pylades persuade his friend to sleep   (Page 38)
            Lights reveal Iphigenia

EFFECTS PLOT

ACT I

To open: *A sudden crack of thunder that is not quite thunder, which echoes*   (Page 1)
  and re-echoes through the hall

Cue 1   Before the sound of thunder has died   (Page 1)
  Mist creeps along the floor

Cue 2   **Calchas:** "First one and then the other, you shall be told."   (Page 2)
  The mist begins to clear

Cue 3   **Boys:** "Blood ... blood ... blood ... blood ... blood!"   (Page 3)
  The earth groans. Thunder

Cue 4   **Thybius:** "... where that damned North wind was still blow-   (Page 6)
  ing."
  Sound of wind blowing

Cue 5   **Agamemnon**, **Menelaus**, **Thybius** and other menacing figures   (Page 8)
  of importance enter
  The wind howls more loudly throughout the scene

Cue 6   **Agamemnon:** "What if the wind does not die?"   (Page 9)
  The wind slowly dies

Cue 7   **Thybius:** "... their left sides no longer wind blasted."   (Page 9)
  A new wind starts until the lights slowly go down

Cue 8   **Thybius:** "Thanks to this little beauty ..."   (Page 16)
  Thunder. Smoke drifts across the stage. The sound of toppling
  buildings. Flames are projected across the acting area

Cue 9   Five times the gongs and drums strike. Then silence   (Page 17)
  Fade flame effect

Cue 10   The rumbling grows louder   (Page 22)
  Sound of a thin wind mingles with the music

ACT II

Cue 11   **Orestes:** "... but to kill a mother!"   (Page 25)
  Low rumble of thunder

Cue 12   **Thybius:** "Here they come now."   (Page 27)
  Rumble of distant thunder. A cold wind rises

Cue 13   **Clytemnestra:** "You shall be made as welcome as if you had."   (Page 31)
  A wind starts blowing

Cue 14   Orestes strikes   (Page 32)
  Red mist pours from the top of the tower

Cue 15   **Pylades:** "She'll come with us!"   (Page 32)
           The wind howls

Cue 16   **Orestes:** "Apollo, O Apollo, save us!"   (Page 33)
           Crash of thunder. The wind dies down

Cue 17   Fanfare   (Page 33)
           Birds sing in the background

Cue 18   **All:** "Save us, save us, Artemis!"   (Page 40)
           A crash of thunder. A howling gale

REHEARSAL AND PRODUCTION NOTES

Why myth?

In all my plays for young people I have concentrated—usually unknow-ingly—on the theme of heroism. In many ways this has run counter to the general trend of drama today, but I firmly believe that what we still crave (individually and collectively) is an identification with something bigger than ourselves, some cause, some theme, some faith that transcends ourselves and gives our life some meaning. To find no meaning in life is to render life meaningless; I believe the search continues in spite of ourselves.

Myth—the great stories which go back to the birth of mankind—is one of the ways this search proceeds. The huge questions which tease and torment us—Who am I? Where did I come from? What is the earth? What are the planets? What is death? Is there a life beyond?—have been asked since the dawning of time, and it is in the myths that some of the (contemporary) answers have been given. There is much in the Agamemnon stories which would prove familiar once we have gone beyond the superficial strangeness of the incidents. Basically the narrative proceeds from retribution through justice to regeneration. Euripides, from whose play *Iphigenia in Tauris* I culled the last scene, even seems to anticipate the Christian precept of rebirth as the result of sacrificing oneself completely. Having offered to die for Pylades, Orestes seems at last to be looking into his own dark soul and finding there—in confronting his destiny—the opportunity of making his split self a unity once more. In sacrifice is his new life. It is only the last-minute discovery that he is Iphigenia's brother which saves his life, but the shadow-self has been embraced and he has accepted himself for what he is.

The Greek dramatists themselves reflected in their plays the changing face of society as they saw it. The nature of the gods, the meaning of revenge, the emergence of justice as a moral precept instead of vengeance and (in *Iphigenia in Tauris*) even a justice tempered with mercy—all these issues were being raised in the society which first saw the performances of the Oresteian plays. Today the same issues worry us. As for the answers, surely they continue to evade us?

The style

From its very inception, we decided that the play should be both timeless and placeless. The test of a great myth is just that. It should apply to everybody, everywhere. Consequently we turned our backs on any restric-tion which would make it specifically Greek. Both the composer and the designers were asked to imagine themselves in some ante-room of pre-history where all the great stories of man were born before the ethnic racial marches took nations to their place on earth. Thus I wanted both Africa and Japan involved. The Peruvian and North American Indians could equally have been represented. The cast and the audience had to understand that this ritualistic examination of the story was also the story of mankind. Out of this search evolved a design *style*, a movement style, and a universal sound of music which were basic and not specific. One other virtue emerged. At least the cast had seen films or photographs of African tribes today. Some had visited Morocco or Israel or Central Africa. By seeing the play in terms of witch-doctors and voodoo, desert and dust, they were able to get a firmer reality on the play than if we had attempted to do it all in terms of Greece over three thousand years ago.

Rehearsals

Nevertheless this called for extensive work on improvisations. Because this was a summer holiday project organized by the Cockpit, rehearsals were an all-day affair over a four-week period. Every morning started off with a physically exhausting limbering session, lasting sometimes an hour, sometimes longer, run either by myself or the assistant director. Boys attended in shorts or swimming trunks, girls in leotards. They relaxed on the floor, leapt for the ceiling, explored space with outflung arms, crawled, did cartwheels, spun in the air, or simply dug into themselves humming or drumming to the sound of their own heartbeats. Basic work on gesture alternated with basic work on voice. The musical director coached them in rhythms so that after the first week they were able to beat out steps on the floor or clap in intricate counts. Improvisations started—both verbal and to music—on what the play meant to them in terms of today. They were encouraged to think of domestic situations or business takeovers or terrorist activities—anything which gave them a reality on the story they were to enact. Early rehearsals soon exposed the need to explore the background. Long discussions and talks (informal) took place about life in primitive communities *today*. The rehearsal space became a village. The young people selected their sleeping-quarters, acted out the events of the day—*where nothing happened*. Quite the most difficult kind of improvisation where they simply had to be, and not do—until the village, their neighbours and they themselves had become acceptable and understandable and real.

New Speech

To encourage this feeling of identification with this new primitive existence, we agreed to avoid the use of English in these village improvisations. Classes took place in New Speech which was simply another name for gibberish. Communication, I explained, usually depends on words whose meaning we take for granted. Young people reading a part usually drone out the words as if words alone will tell us what the play is about. To re-examine the real value, the real weight of words, we invented our own language. "Moon", for example, described that object hanging in the sky, but "loodie" had to be accompanied by an expressive gesture, an exhalation, a "mood" which would make its meaning clear. At first the young people resisted the idea. They felt exposed, vulnerable, very insecure, but as soon as they realized that I wanted an emotional reaction to a request for a new word for "mother", "sky", "sea", and not some vague intellectual abstraction based on some other language they may have learnt, they began to see it as fun.

Nobody was right, nobody was wrong, I had to assure them—just give me a sound, any sound that expresses the idea of "beautiful", "thunder", "river", "fear". Soon they found they could hold conversations with one another, could make requests, even answer questions posed to them by somebody talking equally incomprehensible gobbledegook. Great consternation erupted one day in the "village" when the wives who had been left at home while the men went hunting, discovered a "shoosh" hiding under the audience scaffolding—quite obviously a snake.

The life of the village extended over nearly a week. The boys went hunting, which meant they had to slink, crouch, slide, slither and pounce. A wedding was celebrated, a mother died in child-birth, but generally nothing happened . . . only life. From time to time I would call out the hour of the day . . . "It is now midday, the shadows are small, concentrated under the trees. It is too hot to be out of doors" and so on . . . "Four o'clock, the sun is sinking to the horizon. The shadows are lengthening." To emphasize the "shape of the day", I'd run through twenty-four hours in five minutes, and then in three minutes, and then in thirty seconds, encouraging them to feel the rise and fall of their daily existence.

All this was necessary because I wanted very early to make sure that nobody would ever leave the stage during performance except to make a vitally important costume change. To me (and I've no doubt to any harassed drama teacher) any actor in a dressing-room is a wasted actor. Everybody had to be on stage all the time, which meant that they had to have an attitude to everything which happened in the course of the play. And as they were due to play for two and a half weeks, they had to be able to create afresh each time. I've no doubt that the background we gave them helped them to do just this.

The movement
Because I believe that the voice is only one of the actor's tools, and that the body (particularly in a young actor) is a more powerful one, great emphasis was laid on the physicality of the production. Apart from the strenuous limbering and the movement classes, classes also were held with the Assistant Director in a form of movement called "release", where each member of the cast learnt to make use of body weight allied to relaxation. Inner rhythms were explored, both individually and collectively so that at times the whole cast could move soundlessly and intuitively as one organism. No experience of dance was essential. All that was required was a willingness to have a go. The collective dedication was enough after that. Out of it grew the gradual abandon which moved our North African drumming and wailing from South Kensington certainly as far south as Rabat or even Casablanca. The normal reserve of the English young became quite as erotic as I felt we ought to go.

Difficulties
Only two scenes require mention here. The blocking and pacing of the trial gave great trouble. This was probably because for the first time in the play we had to find an air of serenity. Blood, for once, had run its course. For days this scene remained lax and unhappy. Fortunately I soon discovered

that there were varying opinions about the guilt of Orestes. Had he been justified in killing his mother? Some said one thing, some another. We thereupon decided to hold our own trial. A week was spent in preparation, with leaders of both prosecution and defence lining up their cases. Strange decisions had to be made. Witnesses could be called, including the Pythoness, but not the gods! Orestes could defend himself, but only through question and answer. A jury of twelve don't-knows was appointed, but through some oversight (probably because costume fittings were taking place at the same time) thirteen actually took part in the voting, and Orestes escaped with his life by one vote! I mention this only in the hope that some other director may find it a way to make the cast *think* about the scene they are playing and their attitude to the questions raised. Orestes, for example, pooh-poohed very early on my suggestion that guilt resides in the mind. "But what if you were found guilty of a murder you had not committed?" somebody asked him. "Would you be guilty then?" "Of course not," he replied. "There you are then." After this, all were more prepared to discuss the nature of guilt.

The other scene which gave trouble was the ending. The scene as we played it—almost entirely in mime-drama—has not been included in this printed version. It was too light, too abstract, and the story, which had been born of blood, rather faded away. Mercy as a philosophical concept cannot compare dramatically with vengeance, I'm afraid. In this present version I have tried to compensate for that. However, a director is warned about this danger. Too light an interpretation can make it a play which ends two-thirds of the way through. The issue of Orestes' fate must be kept imperative to the end.

Further reading

Two books on myth have been recommended as suitable for young minds: William Mayne's *A Game of Dark* (Hamish Hamilton), and Ursula Leguin's *The Wizard of Earthsea* (H.E.B. New Windmill Series).

Finally

The use of quotations from *Hamlet* is deliberate, as I hope the inverted commas show. I have always been fascinated by the parallel between Orestes and the Prince of Denmark. The quotations from *The Merchant of Venice* seem equally apposite, but may be more difficult to spot.

                                                                              J.W.

MADE AND PRINTED IN GREAT BRITAIN BY
LATIMER TREND & COMPANY LTD PLYMOUTH

MADE IN ENGLAND